Edison

THOMAS ALVA EDISON

Edison

By

REX BEASLEY

Foreword by Herbert Hoover

CHILTON BOOKS

A DIVISION OF CHILTON COMPANY
Publishers
Philadelphia and New York

To My Brothers-In-Law

JACK SANFORD

ROBERT SANFORD

WILBUR SANFORD

Thomas Edison, who believed that "everything comes to him who hustles," would have admired their character and industriousness.

WORKS BY THE AUTHOR

Biography

EDISON

Religious

PAGEANT OF A KING
A Story of The Christ

Novelette

THE GREEN KNOLL

Plays

THE SPLENDOR OF THREE

Essays

NEW LEAF OR OLD BELIEF
WITH MY LITTLE HATCHET
WHAT ARE WE CELEBRATING?

History

GREAT MEN OF HISTORY SKETCHES:
THOMAS A. EDISON
MARK TWAIN
ABRAHAM LINCOLN
WILL ROGERS
SPENCER TRACY
HENRY FORD
ROBERT E. LEE
GEORGE GERSHWIN
GARY COOPER
ANDREW JACKSON
SAM HOUSTON
LUTHER BURBANK
THOMAS JEFFERSON
RICHARD RODGERS
BABE RUTH
BENJAMIN FRANKLIN
WALT DISNEY
THEODORE ROOSEVELT
CECIL B. DE MILLE
GEORGE WASHINGTON
KENNETH ROBERTS
VICTOR HERBERT
DANIEL BOONE
ORVILLE AND WILBUR WRIGHT

Acknowledgements

THE AUTHOR WISHES *to thank the following individuals and organizations for their assistance in the writing of this book. Each of them has been most cooperative and helpful, making this project of Edison's life an extreme pleasure.*

CHARLES EDISON, *son of the late inventor, for his generous help and interest in this chronicle of his father's career. His kindness in checking the authenticity of Edison's quotations as used in this book, is deeply appreciated.*

HERBERT HOOVER, *for the foreword to this book, an enduring expression of esteem for his friend Thomas Edison.*

HARVEY S. FIRESTONE, JR., *Chairman of the Board of The Firestone Tire & Rubber Company, for his assistance with illustrative material and permission to quote from a letter written by naturalist John Burroughs to Harvey S. Firestone in a limited edition of "In Nature's Laboratory."*

FRANCIS JEHL, *the late laboratory assistant of Edison's, for his encouragement of the author over the years. This grand old man remained, until his death in 1941, a steadfast friend and a source of inspiration for this story.*

THE FORD MOTOR COMPANY *of Dearborn, Michigan, and its Research Department, for illustrations of Edison's Menlo Park laboratory as restored at Greenfield Village.*

THE HENRY FORD MUSEUM AND GREENFIELD VILLAGE *of Dearborn, Michigan, for an illustration por-*

traying the re-enactment, during Light's Golden Jubilee, of the invention of the electric lamp in Edison's restored Menlo Park laboratory at Greenfield Village.

McGRAW-EDISON COMPANY *of Elgin, Illinois, for illustrative and invaluable research material concerned with the Edison story.*

GENERAL ELECTRIC COMPANY *of Schenectady, New York, for illustrations involving various phases of Edison's life and work.*

THE UNITED STATES DEPARTMENT OF THE IN-TERIOR, *in charge of the West Orange, New Jersey, Edison National Historic Site, for priceless research data and illustrations.*

To each of these, the author is grateful for permission to use the material which has helped re-create the story of Thomas Alva Edison within these pages.

Rex Beasley

Harris & Ewing

Foreword

BY HERBERT HOOVER

DARKNESS IS *a forbidden limitation upon righteous human activities.*

When Mr. Edison invented the electric lamp he may perhaps have thought just to produce plain light and more of it at less cost. I surmise that his wildest ambition was to relieve the human race from the curse of always cleaning oil lamps, scrubbing up candle drips, and everlastingly carrying one or the other of them about.

The electric lamp has found infinite variety of unexpected uses. It enables us to postpone our spectacles for a few years longer; it has made reading in bed infinitely more comfortable; by merely pushing a button we have introduced the element of surprise in dealing with burglars; the goblins that lived in dark corners and under the bed have now been driven to the out-doors; evil deeds which inhabit the dark have been driven back into the farthest retreats of the night; it enables the doctor to peer into the recesses of our insides; it substitutes for the hot-water bottle in aches and pains; it enables our cities and towns to clothe themselves in gaiety by night, no matter how sad their appearance may be by day. And by all its multiple uses it has lengthened the hours of our active lives, decreased our fears, replaced the dark with good cheer, increased our safety, decreased our toil, and enabled us to read the type in the telephone book. It has become the friend of man and child.

In making this, as in his other great inventions, Mr. Edison gave an outstanding illustration of the value of the modern method and system of invention, by which highly equipped, definitely organized laboratory research transforms the raw material of scientific knowledge into new tools for the hand of man. We must constantly strengthen the fiber of national life by the inculcation of that veracity of thought which springs from the search for truth. From its pursuit we shall discover the unfolding of beauty, we shall stimulate the aspiration for knowledge, we shall ever widen human understanding.

Mr. Edison gave a long life to such service. Every American owes a debt to him. It is not alone a debt for great benefactions he brought to mankind, but also a debt for the honor he brought to our country. Mr. Edison by his own genius and effort rose from modest beginnings to membership among the leaders of men.

His life gives renewed confidence that our institutions hold open the door of opportunity to all those who would enter.

Herbert Hoover

Contents

Edison

Edison conversing with industrialist Harvey Firestone

sey, had come untold advances in chemistry and industrial progress. The old man was revered as a tinkering genius, and those close about him dared not dispute his findings. Few indeed criticized the work or philosophy of Thomas Alva Edison. In his laboratory his word was law and to violate this law would likely mean unemployment.

"My philosophy of life is work," he would shout. "All I ask of a man is that he have honest convictions and principles and live by them."

His heavy brows would come together in sternness and his employees had no doubts as to his own convictions. Every day he would punch the company time clock as an example for his workers. They stood in awe of their formidable employer and scurried to their workbenches in haste. Loitering was not tolerated and a full day's work was expected from every man.

Because of his tremendous deafness, everyone shouted at him. With a hand cupped to his ear, he would strain to catch every word. In his laboratory, he was the exalted head and he fully intended to keep abreast of every project.

One day the old man was asked when he planned to retire. He stood silent for a moment, then shouted his reply.

"The day before the funeral!"

He required very little sleep and would return to work immediately. Many times he slept on a worktable, waking as refreshed as though he had a full night's rest. His energy was unfailing which made it difficult for younger men to keep up with him.

He was forever concerned with time and crammed every hour in studying or experimenting. Edison felt that mankind was still on the threshold of discovery.

"We are just beginning to scratch the surface," he exclaimed. "I am interested in Einstein — but I can't understand a thing he says. I am the zero in mathematics, but I don't have to moan over it any more, since I found out through my questionnaire that professors of Harvard and Yale are as ignorant as I am."

Presentation of a gold medal to Edison by The Argentina Association of Electrical Engineers, 1930

Many times he said he would prefer life on Mars to earth, because that planet had a longer day than ours. He pushed and prodded untiringly and often it was midnight before his associates could talk with him. He never carried a watch and considered time the most valuable thing in the world.

Honors from around the world had been heaped upon him. He paid them little mind and kept pace with his rigid schedule. After a lengthy day's work, he would retire to his home in nearby Llewellyn Park. The house, a sprawling structure named Glenmont, sat on a well-guarded thirteen acre tract. Inside, the residence was elaborately furnished in the Victorian tradition and was the hub of his family life.

His wife, the former Mina Miller, often played the piano for him in the evenings. He would sit slumped over and listen intently. One hand was always cupped at his ear so that the strains of music could reach him. As she played the music of Beethoven, the old man became absorbed.

"Beethoven — my favorite composer! His Ninth Symphony is the world's greatest masterpiece," he would say. "Some day I am going to preserve it on my phonograph records. When I have done that, I am willing to quit."

On the second floor of Glenmont, Edison had a den. Here, surrounded by mementos and family photographs, he would pore over new ideas. It was a place of relaxation for him. He was proud of his mansion and it reminded him of his climb to success over the years. The house itself seemed to reflect strength, with its gabled roofs and stained glass windows; gardens of flowers and stone benches set off the huge rust-colored home of brick and clapboard. It was one of the finest showplaces in West Orange — this private lair of the Wizard's.

Edison had many friends. Among his closest companions were Harvey Firestone, Henry Ford and John Burroughs. The four famous men found great enjoyment in one another's company and often made camping trips together. They would travel by automobile (Fords, of course) and seek the privacy of the country. Tents were pitched for sleeping and their food was

Edison and Harvey Firestone relax on a camping trip

Courtesy Firestone Tire & Rubber Company

prepared under the open sky. There was always a round of jokes and a great deal of idea exchange among the men. In a recorded diary of one of the trips, John Burroughs made some interesting comments about the great Edison.

"It was a great pleasure to see Edison relax and turn vagabond so easily, sleeping in his clothes, curling up at lunch time on a blanket under a tree and dropping off to sleep like a baby, getting up to replenish the camp-fire at daylight or before, and more than that to see him practice what he preaches about our excessive eating and at each meal taking only a little toast and a cup of hot milk.

"The luxuries of our 'Waldorf-Astoria' on wheels that followed us everywhere, had little attraction for Mr. Edison. One cold night he hit on a new way of folding his blankets; he made them interlock so and so, then got into them, 'made one revolution' and the thing was done. Do you remember with what boyish delight he would throw up his arms when we suddenly came upon some particularly striking view? I have to laugh when I think of the incident of the big car two girls were driving down a wet slippery street in Saranac and which when the driver put on the brakes suddenly changed ends and stopped leaving the amazed girls looking up the street instead of down. 'Organized matter,' remarked Mr. Edison, 'sometimes behaves in a very strange manner.' "

Edison had a great respect for nature and regarded it as a storehouse of discovery. He was continuously probing its secrets, hoping to convert them for use by man. Naturally, he was often queried about his beliefs in God or the Divine Creator. The old man at one time was asked directly if he did believe in a God. His reply was short and pointed.

"Certainly! The existence of such a God can, to my mind, almost be proved from chemistry."

He paused, stroking his chin in further thought. Then, glancing heavenward, he continued.

"I know this world is ruled by Infinite Intelligence. It required Infinite Intelligence to create it and it requires Infinite

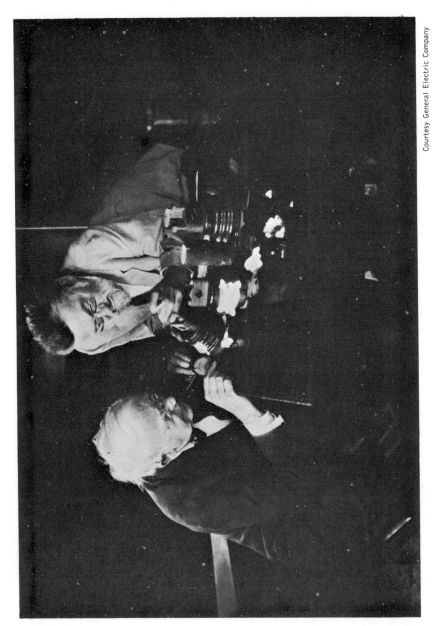

Edison visits the electrical genius, Charles Steinmetz, at General Electric

Intelligence to keep it on its course. Everything that surrounds us — everything that exists — proves that there are Infinite Laws behind it. There can be no denying this fact — it is mathematical in its precision."

His good friend and camping partner, Harvey Firestone, tells us that Edison spoke to him about God. Shortly after the death of President Harding, the old man had this remark to make.

"I believe in the teachings of our Lord and Master. There is a great directing head of people and things — a Supreme Being who looks after the destinies of the world! I am convinced that the body is made up of entities that are intelligent and are directed by this Higher Power."

He then peered with his bright eyes into the face of Firestone. His deliberate voice talked on.

"When one cuts his finger, I believe it is the intelligence of these entities which brings convalescence. You know that there are living cells in the body so tiny that the microscope cannot find them at all. The entities that give life and soul to the human body are finer still and lie infinitely beyond the reach of our finest scientific instruments. When the entities leave the body, the body is like a ship without a rudder — deserted, motionless and dead."

Because of his intense interest in science, many believed that Edison was an agnostic. In his earlier years it was true that he gave little thought to the matter of eternal life. As age crept up on him, the old man gave more serious attention to the subject of religion; but his chief concern was the present life and the work being done in the areas of research and experimentation. To him, it was almost a part of religion itself.

On occasion, Edison would visit with other minds engaged in work similar to his own. He greatly admired the electrical scientist, Charles Steinmetz of General Electric, and found the little hunchback an interesting conversationalist. When the old inventor visited Steinmetz in Schenectady, he was fascinated with his experiments in the field of artificial lightning; he sat amazed as great bolts of flashing light jumped from huge equipment, dashing down upon miniature houses and buildings. The gnarled Steinmetz was studying the results of lightning and a solution to protect men and property from its devastation. Naturally, Edison supported Steinmetz's humanitarian research and felt comfortable with him, because "he never mentioned mathematics when he talked to me."

Even though he could be stubborn and even tyrannical about his work, Edison possessed a spirit of kindness. He was once informed that the daughter of a friend was seriously ill and confined to her room. He paid a visit to the child, finding her in low spirits. The sun shone through the window of her room and she looked longingly at the beautiful day. Edison promised the sick child a picnic on his next visit. She realized that it would be impossible to leave her bed, but he assured her of the picnic as promised.

Several days passed before he returned. The little girl was delighted to see him. He entered the room, bearing a large wicker basket. He laughed and patted her hand in greeting. The picnic, he said, was about to begin. From the interior of the basket, he withdrew all manner of food and several strange bottles.

"Where would you like to have the picnic?" he asked. "In the mountains — by the seashore?"

The girl laughed. "But I cannot go," she replied.

Edison smiled. "Through the magic of these bottles we can pretend," he said. "The vapor from one bottle has the aroma of mountain air . . . another is like the scent of the sea."

So it was that the pair enjoyed an indoor picnic together. The food was spread out upon the bed and when the child decided upon an illusionary seashore, an appropriate bottle was opened and a fresh vapor filled the room. In imagination, the old man and child were miles away from the sick room. After his visit, the girl improved rapidly and in no time was well.

It was Edison's kindness and interest that inspired Henry Ford. In the year 1896, Ford was chief engineer of the Detroit Edison Company. He had just built his first automobile. The

Edison Company held a convention close to New York and Ford hoped to get near the great Edison during the meeting. He desired an interview so that he might tell the inventor about his automobile. One night, after a dinner for the employees, a friend introduced Ford to Edison. For several minutes the two bent their heads together in conversation. Ford explained the principle of his automobile with excited gestures. After hearing him out, Edison banged his fist upon the table.

"Young man," he shouted, "that's the thing — you have it. Keep at it."

Ford was elated and from that time on, his career was devoted to the improvement of his automobile. Never during his lifetime did he forget the kindness of Thomas Edison and the two were friends until the inventor's death.

In his own work, Edison had been the victim of criticism for years. Professional scientists disdained his methods of experimentation. His was one of trial and error. If one idea did not achieve results, then he tried another. In his search for the electric light, Edison plodded through 9,990 separate experiments. He kept record books in which he noted failures as well as achievements, carefully writing them out in his own hand.

But criticism was not new to the old man in the black suit. Since his early childhood, there had always been stories about his unusual behavior. He was many times the center of derision and jeerings. Everyone close to him resented the attacks upon his personality and character. His parents were, of course, most deeply affected and had been plagued with the problem since his birth.

No doubt Edison reflected many times upon those long-ago days. Shuffling about his laboratory in his later years, the hazy scenes of the past would return. Instead of an elderly inventor, the dream of a young boy would float through the masterful mind. The picture of a far distant home might come to him, framed in a scene of ice and freezing snow. He could see a parlor, small and snug, where a lone man sat in solitude; and as the picture came more into focus, he recognized the solitary man who gazed far away upon a frozen landscape.

The man was Samuel Edison, his father, and his preoccupation was over his youngest son.

Let us return, for but a fleeting moment, to the village of Port Huron and the youthful beginnings of Thomas Alva Edison. It is deep winter and the snows have just fallen as we join a lone man and his thoughts.

The Frozen Frontier

RUBY RED COALS burned brightly in the iron stove.

An occasional sputter of flame would flare up, then die down quietly. The room itself was tiny and in no time had gotten as warm as toast. Outside the house, great gusts of snow blew into the air and the entire countryside lay buried beneath a blanket of white. For many years now, the winters in Michigan had increased in their bitterness. The settlers in the area made careful plans in advance of the freezing onslaught and were prepared for a long, solitary siege.

To the man sitting in the small cramped room, this was of little importance. He had made provision for the winter and, more important, for his family. Samuel Edison might be foolhardy in many ways, but he loved his wife and children and never failed them. Now, looking out the ice-coated window, he felt content. Great forests loomed in the distance and lumber camps dotted the hills. Across the frozen land he could hear the cries of lumberjacks and the thunder of trees felled upon the ground. He had moved his family into this wonderland of ice and had never once regretted it.

Back in Milan, Ohio — their old home town — he felt that better opportunity awaited him at the hustling village of Port Huron. Here he had set up in business as a lumber and grain merchant. Nearby was the gray choppy lake which offered convenient transportation for goods and made Port Huron a busy hustling settlement. There was no doubt about it, success lay just around the corner for Samuel and his wife, Nancy. Even the children would benefit by being citizens of this place; the oldest was

Samuel Edison, Edison's father

Nancy Edison, Edison's mother

a bright boy named William Pitt, a fine sprout of a lad who surely would make his way; next in order was a daughter, Tannie, who quietly followed her mother about the house; then there was the youngest, a son impressively named Thomas Alva who also held the distinction of being the family problem child.

As Samuel Edison sat alone, he almost dozed off thinking about this youngest child. Ever since the boy's birth in February of 1847, the Edisons had experienced seven years of heartache. For one thing, the head of the youngster was slightly oversize and was filled with all manner of mischief. Every day he plied his mother with questions which made no sense at all, and except for her patience, would have driven her to distraction. Luckily, she had been a schoolmarm before marrying Samuel and had learned the art of patience with young folk; because of this experience, she gently answered the boy's curious questions and encouraged him to observe the world in which he lived. Thomas Alva deeply loved his mother. His little fingers would caress her smooth face as he peered with his large eyes into hers.

"I love you, Mama," he would exclaim and hug her tight.

The relationship between young Thomas and his father had been of a more strained nature. Back in the old home town of Milan, the boy had caused the family a great deal of embarrassment. Time and again Samuel punished his youngest son for his wayward, and often curious, deeds. On one occasion, Tom had set fire to the barn just to see what would happen; in no time, the dry wood flamed into the sky and the building was scorched. For this misadventure, Tom was rewarded with a public spanking by his father.

Then there had been the episode of the Seidlitz powders. The boy decided that humans could fly if inflated with gas. He recruited a neighbor chum, Michael Oates, to assist him in the experiment. Carefully Tom mixed the powders in a glass of water and bade young Oates to swallow it. Instead of taking flight, the boy fell to the ground with agonizing stomach pains. Again, Tom was spanked for his deed.

Young Edison was still determined to put a human being into

the air. For his next experiment, he chose the family chore girl. She stood by anxiously as the lad explained his theory. It seemed to him that all birds ate worms and that this delicacy enabled them to fly; he then proceeded to mix a generous supply of worms with water and asked the girl to drink it. She did as her young charge insisted and immediately was nauseated. Again, Tom was led into the public square by his father and was spanked.

Then there had been the case of the goose eggs. Tom felt that if mother geese could hatch their eggs, then so could he. His father found him one day sitting on a nest, patiently waiting for the little fowls to hatch. The result of this curious experiment was another round of punishment and a stained pair of trousers.

Samuel Edison thought of all of these things in the quiet of the room. He got to his feet and walked to the stove. The embers glowed brightly within its bowels and sent a warm feeling over the man. In the next room, he could hear the murmur of voices. It was his wife instructing young Tom in his schoolwork. Samuel sighed to himself, taking his place beside the window once more. As he gazed out across the frozen land, he recalled the visit of the schoolteacher several months ago.

The visit had been brief and to the point. Mr. and Mrs. Edison were told that their son was addled, that his mind was weak and wandering. The teacher warned that the child could no longer attend classes. At this point, Mrs. Edison lost her temper and shouted that she would teach her son. She ushered the teacher to the door in a frenzy of anger.

Since that time, Nancy Edison had devoted many hours to the education of young Tom. By the age of nine, and with his mother's guidance, he had read Gibbon's "Decline and Fall of the Roman Empire," Sears' "History of the World," Hume's "History of England," Burton's "Anatomy of Melancholy," and the "Dictionary of Sciences."

He loved to study geography and English. Hours were spent on correct penmanship and his handwriting resembled a copperplate engraving. Of all his subjects, Tom found mathematics the most difficult and trying. In later years he once commented on his feeling for math.

"I can always hire some mathematicians," he chuckled, "but they can't hire me."

The companionship with his mother established a strong bond between them. Tom never forgot the cheerful hours Nancy devoted to him. As an old man, he praised her with warmth and love.

"I discovered in early life," he mused, "what a good thing a mother was. When she came out as my strong defender, when the school-teacher called me 'addled,' I determined then that I would be worthy of her and show her that her confidence was not misplaced. She was so true, so sure of me. I felt that I had someone to live for, someone I must not disappoint. She was always kind and sympathetic and never seemed to misunderstand or misjudge me."

The old man would then pause, his eyes misty. Blowing his nose into a wrinkled handkerchief he continued.

"The good effects of her early training I can never lose. If it had not been for her appreciation and her faith in me at a critical time in my experience, I should very likely never have become an inventor. You see, she believed that many of the boys who turned out badly by the time they grew to manhood would have become valuable citizens if they had been handled in the right way when they were young. Her years of experience as a school-teacher taught her many things about human nature and especially about boys. I was always a careless boy, and with a mother of a different character I should have probably turned out badly. But her firmness, her sweetness, her goodness, were potent powers to keep me in the right path."

The old man's voice might quiver at this point as he wiped at his nose. "The memory of her will always be a blessing to me," he concluded, returning to his work once more and the memory of his mother.

As a child, it was not all study. Many precious hours were

spent in the basement of the Edison homestead. Here, in the musty coolness of the cellar, young Tom established his first laboratory. He had a workbench where he worked with his chemicals and crude equipment. Many bottles lined the wooden shelves and each was labeled "Poison." Tom had done this to keep the neighborhood children from tampering with his chemicals. Actually, he was familiar with the contents of each bottle through a code system he had worked out. Hour after hour he would perform simple experiments which revealed the wonders of nature to him, as they unfolded before his very eyes.

Electricity, in these days, was regarded as a mysterious force and most people were wary of it. A few pioneers in electrical research were studying the uses of the medium for industry. Samuel Morse had invented the telegraph, which was regarded as a modern miracle. Poles and wires crisscrossed over America, clicking out messages second after second. The telegraph had become the voice of the land, as well as a wealthy industry.

Young Edison was fascinated with the invention. Here, in the confines of the cellar, he built a telegraph set for himself. He strung a wire from his own home to that of a neighbor boy and the two exchanged messages. The telegraph was operated by two batteries and the wires fairly hummed day after day.

To help out with family finance, Young Edison decided to go into the produce business. He got hold of a wagon and horse, then loaded the old wagon with vegetables from his father's garden. Michael Oates (the recovered victim of the Seidlitz powders experiment) traveled from house to house with Tom. In one year, they sold six hundred dollars' worth of produce. But as time went by, Edison decided to get another job. He and Oates dissolved the partnership and went their separate ways.

Tom was now twelve years of age. To him, a wonderful world existed beyond the confines of Port Huron. He had just begun to sell newspapers on the streets of the village and felt that he could do the same on the Grand Trunk Railway; passengers traveling to Detroit should prove to be good customers and sales

Courtesy Department of the Interior, National Park Service

Tom Edison at the age of fourteen

should be excellent. Mrs. Edison was concerned that the train might be wrecked and that her son would be injured or killed. Mr. Edison felt that he, himself, was the family breadwinner and needed no help from Tom. Finally — and with great misgivings — they both agreed to let the boy try.

It was 1859. America was on the brink of industrial expansion. The railroad was one of the richest businesses in the country. Tom was delighted to be a part of it. His hours were convenient, as the train left Port Huron at 7:00 a.m. and pulled into Detroit at 10:00 a.m. There would be a layover until evening and Tom spent his time in the Detroit Public Library studying. The return trip got him home about 9:30 in the evening.

Every day he walked the aisles of the passenger cars selling newspapers, books and candy. Business went well for him. Everyone was fond of the young lad and soon his pockets jingled with a fair income. As an old man, Edison reflected fondly upon those days.

"I well remember the week before Christmas when my train jumped the track near Utica. We had four old Michigan Central cars with rotten sills and they collapsed in the ditch. My supply of candies, figs, dates, raisins, were strewn all over the track."

He paused, his eyes bright with mirth, then continued with a chuckle.

"I hated to see them go to waste, so I attempted to eat them on the spot. The result was that our family doctor had the time of his life."

As time went by, Edison began to miss working in his cellar laboratory. It occurred to him that he might set one up in the baggage car. He spoke to the conductor about it and was given immediate approval. So it was that, after making his sales rounds, the boy would return to his laboratory on wheels. He had much time to think and many of these boyish thoughts were of success. His income was growing and it was only natural to want to earn more. It was then that he conceived the idea of his own newspaper. In Detroit, he found an old secondhand press and — with the reluctant permission of the conductor — brought it aboard

"The Weekly Herald," Edison's newspaper published on The Grand Trunk Railway

the baggage car. He was now engaged in the newspaper business.

All along the route the train paused at stations. At each station there was always a telegrapher and it was through them that Tom got the latest news, "hot off the wire." He rushed back to his printing press, set the type, then rolled off copies of his newspaper called "The Weekly Herald." It proved to be popular with the passengers and ultimately brought Tom more income.

Then the tragedy struck. One day, as the train rolled toward Detroit, it lurched suddenly. Some of the bottles in Tom's laboratory fell to the floor and immediately ignited. In no time, flames sprang up and smoke poured through the baggage car. The conductor, Stevenson, rushed in to combat the fire and when at last it was out, he burst into a rage. The train rattled into Smith's Creek station shortly and Stevenson threw every piece of Tom's laboratory out on the platform. He then turned on the boy and boxed his ears. Legend had it that the boxing caused Edison's deafness, but in later years the old inventor commented otherwise.

"The blow at this time by Stevenson," he reflected, "may have started it, but was finished one day when I was standing on the station platform at Smith's Creek. I was trying to climb into the freight car with both arms full of papers when the conductor, attempting to help me, took me by the ears and lifted me up into the train. I felt something snap inside my head and my deafness started from that time and has ever since progressed."

After the catastrophe, young Edison made an attempt to reconcile himself with the conductor. The stern fellow listened to the lad's plea, finally agreeing to allow him on the train again, but with no laboratory. Once again, Tom hawked his wares of newspapers and sweets aboard the Grand Trunk while confining experiments to his cellar at home.

One morning his train pulled into the Mt. Clemens station to shunt freight. Tom jumped to the platform in order to visit with the station telegrapher, J. U. Mackenzie. The boy had gotten to know the older man during his trips on the railroad. The two were good friends and spent many times together, visiting. This

Replica of the Grand Trunk Train on which Edison worked as a boy

(As restored at the Henry Ford Museum, Dearborn, Michigan)

particular morning was a quiet one, except for the screeching of the freight cars, and Tom looked forward to seeing Mackenzie.

He stepped to the window and hailed the telegrapher. Both were happy to see one another and immediately began to talk. The young son of Mackenzie had been playing about the platform, but had toddled out to the track yard and was standing in the middle of the tracks, fascinated with the shiny rails. As Tom visited with the telegrapher, his eyes shifted to the yards and, with great fright, he saw a boxcar bearing down upon the child. Quickly he dashed to the tracks and jumped toward the boy, pulling him to the ground and out of the way; at that same moment, the boxcar flew past the spot where the boy had been standing.

Mackenzie dashed from the station office in panic. He ran to his young son, embracing him in fear. Tom got to his feet and the trio returned to the platform. Mackenzie clasped young Edison's hand excitedly. In return for saving his son's life, he promised to make a telegraph operator out of Tom and get him a job. This, of course, came as welcome news. Such operators could earn a fair and steady income and Tom was eager to learn.

So it was that he then gave up his job as "newspaper and candy butcher" on the Grand Trunk line and studied telegraphy with Mackenzie. It was not only a reward for saving a life, but proved to be a means of changing his own life. Hours were spent with Mackenzie as the boy grasped the rudiments of telegraphy. He was an apt pupil, quick to learn and anxious to improve. In no time, he found himself prepared to accept his first position as a telegrapher. No longer would his world be limited in scope — the opportunity was here to climb the ladder to success. He did not know at the time what a long ladder it would be or what pitfalls lay ahead of him. He only knew that he wanted to try and to a boy, that can be the first stepping stone to achievement.

Young Tom Edison was ready to tackle the world.

Tinkering Telegrapher

IN HIS WEST ORANGE laboratory — and seventy years away from his telegraphy days — Thomas Edison stood talking with a young man. He was a schoolboy, seeking an interview with the great old man. The aging inventor had interrupted his work for a moment to give the boy his views on life. To the young interviewer, this was a golden opportunity not only to meet the famous man, but to record his philosophies as well.

Edison, still wearing a crumpled flower in his buttonhole, motioned for the boy to take a seat. He ambled slowly about the room gesturing with his arms as he spoke. The youthful reporter scribbled rapidly upon a tablet and found it difficult to keep pace. The revered old man paused to look at his young admirer, a smile slowly spreading across his aging face.

"We live and grow by new knowledge," he said. "The trouble with our way of educating as generally followed is that it does not give elasticity to the mind. It casts the brain into a mold. It insists that the child must accept. It does not encourage original thought or reasoning, and it lays more stress on memory than on observation. It breeds fear, and from fear comes ignorance. The seeing of things in the making is what counts. Then the mind can approach the gaining of knowledge without prejudice."

He paused, allowing the young man to catch up with him. It was good, he thought, to be around youngsters like this lad. The entire future of the world depended upon this fresh generation and the old man was happy to assist them. He was silent for a moment, then spoke once again, his brows knitted together.

"I never did anything worth doing by accident; nor did any of my inventions come by accident — they came by work."

As the boy hurriedly scribbled on his tablet, Edison thought of the work it had taken to achieve his own success. There had been no short cut and the problems at times seemed insurmountable. He could easily recall those earlier days when he began as a telegrapher and how much he had sweated and worked. It seemed almost like yesterday when, as a lad with no experience, he had begun studying with Mackenzie back in Mt. Clemens. Time would never dim that memory. It was in that rickety old railroad station that Edison first learned the trade which led him ultimately to a career of invention.

After mastering the telegraph key, under Mackenzie's instruction, young Edison had set out to find his first job. He accepted a position in Canada at a spot called Stratford Junction. He was paid the lavish amount of twenty-five dollars a month. After a short stay in this community, he moved to another small village called Sarnia, on the Grand Trunk line. It was here that he was dismissed and for reasons he later related in his own words.

"The job at Sarnia just suited me, as I could have the whole day to myself. I taught the night yardman my calls so I could get half an hour's sleep now and then between trains. One night I got an order to hold a freight train and replied immediately that I would do it. I rushed out to find the signalman, but before I could find him and get the signal set, the train roared past my station. I ran to the telegraph office and sent the report over the wire. The only reply I got was: 'Hell!' "

Edison shook his white-crowned head as he concluded.

"I knew by instinct that the dispatcher, on the strength of my message that I would hold the train, had permitted another train to leave the last station in the opposite direction. My mind was filled with visions of a head-on collision. There was a lower station near the junction, where the day operator slept. I started for it on foot. The night was dark and I fell into a culvert and was knocked senseless."

The upshot of the story was that the engineers on the two careening trains saw one another in time. The locomotives were brought to a screeching halt and young Edison was summoned later to the main office in Toronto for a bawling out. He took it on the chin, but at the first opportunity, sneaked out of the manager's office and quickly headed for home in the United States.

After this episode, he journeyed — as a tramp telegrapher — over the entire country. His roving jobs took him to Cincinnati, Memphis, Louisville, Fort Wayne, Indianapolis and New Orleans. He lived meagerly, finding that pay was not constant and that many competitive operators were scouring the big cities. It was a rough life and he found himself associating with equally rough characters. Later in life he recollected an incident which took place in Louisville.

"The close of the Civil War," he recalled, "had left everything in a desperate condition. Disorganization reigned supreme. The operators were coming in like derelicts from the war at all hours. One came in one night, drunk, and kicked over the stove; he piled every operator's table on top and tore the switchboard from the wall, smashing the batteries. Then he left the place, well satisfied with his destruction. Another one started to throw pistol cartridges into the flames on the fire grate. These would explode and I was twice hit by bullets."

As the elder Edison looked back on those days, he would sometimes smile to himself. They were times never to be seen again and in ways had been exciting.

"The Southern cities," he remembered, "were wide open at this time. At night I would go with a companion for midnight lunch and find the faro bank running briskly. There were over twenty keno rooms running. One of them that I visited was in a church — the man with the wheel being in the pulpit and the gamblers in the pews."

After many months of wandering and sometimes going without food, Edison decided that he would return to Cincinnati. He stayed here but a short time, then resolved to go home to Port Huron to see his family. Even though their son returned unsuccessful, he was received with open arms and a steaming Thanksgiving dinner. As in his younger days, he held his mother tight and thanked her for everything she had done for him. Mr. Edison, of course, was delighted that his son came home and equally enjoyed every day of his stay.

In a few days, Tom sat down and addressed a letter to a telegrapher friend in Boston, by the name of Milt Adams. He inquired whether there might be an opportunity for him there as an operator. Shortly the letter was answered. Adams begged his friend to come along with haste and so, in response to this encouragement, Edison bade his family good-bye and hopped the next train bound for Boston.

When he arrived in the teeming and historic city, he immediately looked up his friend, Adams. This stalwart companion took him directly to Western Union where Edison was hired without fanfare. The two then rented a hall bedroom in a broken-down lodging place and ate their meals at a boardinghouse a mile away. Edison plunged into his work with fervor and labored eighteen to twenty hours a day.

In the evenings, he pored over a secondhand set of Faraday's works on electrical experiments. During the day, he continued his work at Western Union and sometimes found a few moments to experiment in the office. Although tinkering with chemicals and electrical apparatus fascinated him, it sometimes resulted in danger. Edison in later years recalled a dangerous incident from those Boston days.

"I was experimenting with a large induction coil when I accidentally got hold of both electrodes. It clenched my hands on them so tightly that I couldn't let go. My only chance to get free was to back off so that the battery wire in my hands would pull the cells off the shelf and break the circuit. I shut my eyes and pulled — but the nitric acid splashed all over my face and ran down my back."

He paused, looking at his hands which were now stained with age.

"I rushed to the sink and climbed in, splashing water over my head to dilute the acid and stop the pain. I thought I was being burned alive. When I finally looked at myself in the glass I was a ghastly black and yellow — my skin was thoroughly oxidized.

Boston Feby 3d 69

Received of Samuel W Ropes Jr
The sum of Thirty 30 dollars –
being full amount received from
him ——

Thomas, A. Edison

A handwritten receipt for a loan, signed by Edison during his telegrapher days

My face looked dreadful. My eyes, fortunately, had been closed when the accident took place, or I would have been blinded. The damaged skin peeled off and a new skin began to grow without leaving scars."

Times were tough and bitter, but young Edison labored on and made many friends in Boston. He gave Western Union loyalty and hard work, even though his salary was meager. On one desperate occasion, he borrowed thirty dollars from a Samuel Ropes, Jr., who apparently demanded a receipt; this tiny scrap of paper, written clearly in blue ink, has survived the passage of time. It says, briefly: "Boston Feby 3d, '69 . . . Received of Samuel W. Ropes Jr. The sum of Thirty 30 dollars — being full amount received from him — Thomas A. Edison."

It was told that about this time, Edison spent thirty dollars on a new suit. He wore it proudly to work one day, but ruined it with sulphuric acid. His comment on the episode was short and quiet.

"That's what I get for putting so much money in a suit!"

If the loan from Ropes was to purchase the suit, one might well imagine Edison's feeling about repaying it.

While working at Western Union, an idea had slowly taken form in Edison's brain. Thus far, his tinkering had led him nowhere, but at last he thought of an invention which might make him some money. At nights he worked on it, carefully connecting wires and checking switches. Finally, in October of 1868, the invention of wood, wires and chemical paper was completed. He called it a Vote Recorder.

Simply, it was a device for recording votes for Congress. The main instrument could be set before the governing body, with an individual wire running to the desk of every Congressman. By moving a switch, each could record his vote, this being registered on a chemically treated paper housed in the recorder. Once the device was perfected to Edison's satisfaction, he borrowed some more money and boarded a train for Washington, the invention tucked under his arm.

In Washington, a Congressional committee listened to Edison's arguments for his Vote Recorder. He carefully demonstrated its mechanism and workings, but the committee turned it down. Edison was deflated, unable to understand their decision. The chairman explained to him that "filibustering" was one of the most powerful maneuvering tools of politicians; this Vote Recorder would kill any chance to filibuster — or gain an advantageous position to change votes. Edison shook his head in bewilderment and disappointment.

"Right there," he later commented, "I made myself a pledge — I would never again waste any time in inventing anything that is not of general usefulness to the people, or that people do not want and will not buy."

Edison returned to Boston and promptly forgot the Vote Recorder. After it had been placed on a shelf, he turned his attention to the improvement of stock tickers and in no time, invented a new ticker. He opened a subscription service for investors and started an exchange in the Gold Exchange building. He had forty customers and for a while, the venture proved to be successful.

Because of his apparent genius at tinkering, a friend suggested that Edison give up Boston and head for New York. In that great sprawling city, there could be greater opportunity for success. The young inventor deliberated the suggestion and, in the year 1869, decided to try New York. So it was, that on a cold raw day, Edison sailed by boat from Boston, waving farewell to his friends. He had no money—only ambition—and still felt optimistic about his future. He walked jauntily down the gangplank when the vessel docked in New York. He was twenty-two years of age and knew no one in the vast city. His stomach growled with hunger pains as he left the boat and his first meal was a cup of tea given him by a tea tester in a warehouse. With this warmth inside him, he then set out to look for a job.

As a stoop-shouldered old man, he recalled his feelings on that first day in New York City.

"My first thought after leaving the boat," he said, "was to find some way to get breakfast. I was without sufficient money to obtain it. The journey to Washington with my 'Vote Recorder,' and my experiences with the statesmen at the National Capital, had put me heavily in debt. The funds I had borrowed to develop the 'stock ticker' were gone. Everything I possessed, and everything I had earned since twelve years of age, had been 'invested in acquiring experience and knowledge.' "

He soon met a telegraph operator — one of the vast fraternity — and borrowed one dollar. This he used to purchase food at a restaurant close by the Washington Market. He recollected this meager meal with a touch of sadness.

"I had to make my dollar go a long way, so I ordered apple dumplings and coffee. It seemed to me that I had never eaten anything so good in all my life."

With luck, and a short while later, he gained permission to sleep in the basement of the Gold Indicator Building. This firm manufactured an electrical indicator which recorded stock quotations on the floor of the Gold Exchange. The basement was damp, but Edison's spirits were not, so he found endurance an easy thing. His main problem was that his borrowed dollar had almost been spent. He must find work, but he had no idea where.

As is the way with life, an opportunity presented itself unexpectedly. While Edison was browsing about the basement one day, he heard a great deal of commotion upstairs in the building. The young man rushed up to the main floor and found the place in a state of panic. The transmitter, which relayed quotations to the Gold Exchange, had suddenly broken down.

Dr. S. S. Laws, who was the inventor of the transmitter and vice president of the Gold Exchange, was most excited. He roared and paced, wanting to know what had happened. No one could tell him. Edison stood apart for a moment, then spoke up.

"I think I can fix it," he volunteered.

Dr. Laws pounded on a table, his face purple with excitement.

"Fix it! Fix it! Be quick about it!" he shouted.

Edison went to the instrument and found that a spring had broken and had jammed two gear wheels. He worked silently for a long period of time, paying little attention to the cries of Dr.

Edison's printing stock ticker, manufactured at Newark in 1871

Laws. Finally, and with a sigh of relief from the crowd, the instrument started clicking and service was restored.

Dr. Laws was naturally impressed with the young stranger's ability. The next day, he sent for Edison and made the penniless young man an offer. It was to take charge of the entire plant at a salary of $300 a month. Edison was virtually stunned. Edison quickly accepted the job and labored for the firm until it later merged with the Gold and Stock Telegraph Company, which then was purchased by Western Union.

In the October 1, 1869 issue of the "Telegrapher," there appeared a small neatly printed ad. It announced the newly created firm of "Pope, Edison & Co. — Electrical Engineers and General Telegraph Agency." Edison had met young Pope at the Gold Indicator Company and after the merger, decided to go into business with him. As time went by and the partners established a flourishing trade, General Marshall Lefferts — president of Western Union — observed them carefully. When Edison and Pope brought out a new and improved Gold Printer, Lefferts bought it for Western Union. The two men afterward turned out invention after invention, but with not much success. Then Edison himself invented what he termed a Universal Printer. This immediately came to General Lefferts' attention and Edison was asked to come to the office of Western Union. Lefferts looked at him boldly.

"How much do you want for your Universal Printer?" he asked.

Edison had already thought that $5,000 would be ample for the invention. But now, standing before the stern Lefferts, he decided to drop to $3,000. At last, and with a quiver to his voice, young Edison spoke up.

"General, why don't you make me an offer?"

The room was quiet for a long moment. General Lefferts looked gruff and upset, but finally rose from his desk. He addressed Edison calmly.

"How would $40,000 strike you?" he inquired.

Edison almost fainted from shock. He had never in his wildest dreams expected to be paid such a sum. He remained stunned

Mary Stilwell as she appeared in 1871

for a moment, then in a weak voice, answered General Lefferts.

"I think that is fair," he said, grasping the side of the desk for support. Lefferts quickly drew up the contract and made out a check. Edison accepted it with an almost shaking hand. He thanked the General and hurried off to the bank with what seemed a small fortune in his pocket. After cashing the check — and with his coat bulging with bills — he set off to open a shop of his own. He then dissolved his partnership with Pope and commenced to invent on his own.

His shop cost him a great deal of money and finally, because of debts, Edison was compelled to close it down. Still not discouraged, he started building stock tickers again for General Lefferts and moved to a large plant in Newark,. New Jersey. He employed a force of two hundred fifty men, serving as foreman himself. In six years' time, he filed 122 patents, including those for the automatic telegraph, the duplex, quadruplex, sextuplex and multiplex telegraph systems. He was riding the crest of success and had attracted the attention of other inventors in the country.

Then tragedy struck.

For several years, now, Edison's mother had been ill. Since he had left home, the tender lady had become an invalid. Her whole life was wrapped up in her son and week after week, she patiently waited for letters from him. Lying in a snug but confining bed, she read them with tears in her eyes. Tom was surely making a place for himself in the world and her pride fairly burst from her heart. So it was, that on a day in 1871, Thomas Edison was unexpectedly notified that his beloved mother had passed away. He was so grief stricken that a number of years passed before he could mention her name. When he did, it was brief and quickly spoken.

"The memory of her," he whispered, "will always be a blessing to me."

Thus Nancy Edison passed from life, but not from her son's memory. The once strong hands would never squeeze his again; the sparkling eyes were forever closed in sleep and the gentleness of her voice would never reach his ear. But in young Edison's heart, the image of Nancy survived and inspired him in many difficult times.

But nature has a way of balancing things and after his mother died, a young woman entered his life. Her name was Mary G. Stilwell. She was an attractive young girl who worked in Edison's Newark shop. Because his experiments were currently concerned with telegraphy, he had hired the girl technician to assist him in his work; he and Mary labored side by side on the development of a paraffin paper for telegraphic use. In effect, they became very close.

Many months passed. Edison soon discovered that he was madly in love with Mary Stilwell. One day, almost in desperation, he finally asked her to marry him.

"That is," he stammered, "if you will have me."

She was thrilled beyond belief. All the while her young employer had been admiring her, she knew that she in turn loved him. And now, thanks to her prayers, she was to become Mrs. Thomas Alva Edison. She demurely accepted his proposal and in 1873, the couple were happily married. Life was just beginning for Tom and Mary. They stood on the threshold of a new day and a brilliant career for the tousled headed inventor.

But difficult problems besieged Edison and he knew that it was time to leave Newark. His inventions had begun to mount and his time was limited for experimentation. Financial problems had begun to haunt him and he felt he should set up his own laboratory elsewhere. Seclusion, he felt, was necessary for him to work successfully. Thus he scoured the countryside for a good building location and finally, after careful thought, decided upon Menlo Park, New Jersey.

Menlo Park was a quiet green hamlet nestled in the hills. It was situated but twenty-five miles from New York and claimed a small railroad station. A few homes were dotted around the tiny settlement and the population was small. It appealed to Edison, so he promptly purchased some land upon which to build his laboratory. With great delight, he told Mary that he had found a fine old home for them at Menlo Park; she was excited over his plans and hurriedly began packing. Newark was too busy for her and she eagerly looked forward to a quiet life with her young husband.

It was now 1876. The world had no idea what a historic move the Edisons were making. The name of Menlo Park meant nothing at that time; but in the next few years, its fame would be universal, as would that of its new resident. Indeed, Thomas Alva Edison was to become the Wizard of Menlo Park.

Now, to the old man in his laboratory at West Orange, those days were like yesterday. Looking at the young interviewer before him, the elder Edison smiled. He put his hands in wrinkled trouser pockets and walked over to the young boy. The lad was still scribbling upon the tablet. His pencil flew over the blue-ruled lines as Edison laughed. He was delighted to see such an industrious youth and it was a pleasure to relate his own philosophy to him.

The old man tapped the boy gently upon the arm.

"The three great essentials to achieve anything worthwhile," he mused, "are first, hard work; second, stick-to-itiveness; third, common sense."

The lad wrote hurriedly as the aging inventor continued.

"When I want to discover something, I begin by reading up everything that has been done along that line in the past — that's what all these books in the library are for."

He paused to sweep his arm toward the shelves of well-thumbed volumes. The boy looked up in deep admiration before the old man continued. Then the voice of Edison went on, expounding his theory of success.

"I see what has been accomplished at great labor and expense in the past. I gather the data of many thousands of experiments as a starting point, and then I make thousands more."

Standing here now in his twilight years, Edison looked down upon the boy. It would be impossible for the lad to know how many experiments he had performed over a lifetime. But the elder Edison recollected with a sigh the tremendous tasks which faced him back in 1876 when, with a new young wife, he had gone to

Menlo Park. They had been hard days, but he did not regret one of them.

When at last the interview was concluded, Edison led the lad to the door. He shook hands firmly and thanked the boy for coming. The youngster, his tablet clutched tightly, bade the old man farewell. For a long time afterward, Edison stood by his worktable, thinking of the things he had said. It was strange how real the past could become. Menlo Park now seemed but like yesterday and the aged inventor could almost hear the hum of machinery in the old laboratory.

Edison then ambled toward a chair and sat down, his head sunk in meditation. Soon, visions of the once thriving laboratory filled his head and before he knew it, he was sound asleep. As if in a dream, the early years came back like a motion picture, flickering dimly in the old man's brain. Menlo Park had come back to life once again.

Miracles At Menlo Park

SAWS BUZZED AND hammers flew. Great long forms of wood were hoisted into position as the building took shape. It was a rectangular structure, much like a tabernacle, with two floors and a balcony over the front porch. The laboratory was built of clapboard which could endure the bitter New Jersey winters and the onslaught of spring rains.

As construction progressed, the residents of Menlo Park passed by in wonderment. They knew very little about this Thomas Edison, and even less about his work. Research of a scientific nature was unknown to most folk and they were sometimes wary of it. But regardless of such feelings, the building of Edison's laboratory continued.

Wires were strung from telegraph poles directly to the building. Christie Street, which ran alongside Edison's tract of land, became heavily traveled with workmen and equipment. Activity began early in the morning and continued until nightfall when lamps shone from windows, winking in the dusk.

Mary Edison was meanwhile getting settled in their new home. She dusted and scrubbed, swept and polished. She seldom saw her energetic husband until long after dark. Then, after a kiss, they would chatter about their occupations during the day. How was the laboratory coming? Was the water well back of the house sufficient? Did the equipment come down from New York City? How did the little mahogany table look in the bedroom? Their dialogue was filled to the brim with excitement and anticipation.

In a short while, the laboratory was finished. It was a remark-

Edison's Menlo Park Laboratory

(As restored at Henry Ford's Greenfield Village, Dearborn, Michigan)

The second floor of Edison's Menlo Park Laboratory

(As restored at Henry Ford's Greenfield Village, Dearborn, Michigan)

able center of research for its day, fully equipped with all sorts of gadgets and chemicals. The first floor housed a small office, an analytical nook and a machine shop; on the second floor — where miracles were to take place — were several worktables and a chest of drawers. A sink was installed behind the chest and all four walls were lined with shelves, from the floor to the ceiling; these contained all manner of bottles and pieces of apparatus. A pot-bellied stove sat midway in the laboratory to dispel the cold in winter. At the far end of the room rested a small pipe organ, which was to be used for midnight rest breaks and boisterous singing.

It was a marvel to behold, this laboratory of Edison's. From the long multipaned windows, one could gaze out upon the New Jersey countryside, green in summer and white with snow in winter. At night, gas jets supplied the lighting for the shop, flickering dimly over the worktables. From the front balcony of the laboratory could be seen Sarah Jordan's boardinghouse where some of Edison's men lodged; beyond, and down the hill on Christie Street, the home of the young inventor dominated the landscape. Truly, the face of Menlo Park had changed.

When Edison left Newark, he brought with him several men from his old shop. In addition to these, others were hired to assist him in his experiments. Before long, the laboratory was a hive of activity and his staff plunged directly into their work. Edison personally gave his attention to the new telephone, recently invented by Alexander Graham Bell. The original telephone used but one instrument for both transmitting and receiving sound; this, at best, was faint and voices could not be heard at any great distance. Edison set about to improve this situation and created a separate carbon transmitter which increased the voice volume and projected it farther. When finished, he applied for a patent on the transmitter, then turned to other projects in which he was interested.

Because of his youthful experiences as a telegrapher, he maintained a vivid interest in this fascinating field. At Menlo Park, he invented an automatic telegraphic repeater, an instrument that recorded signals in Morse code and repeated them simultaneously to one or more stations at the same time. It sat on a table at the far end of the laboratory and resembled two turntables with flat punctuated discs; one day, quite by accident, an overload of current was sent through the machine, causing it to spin the discs at a high speed. Suddenly, the repeater seemed to chatter in high squealing tones. Edison was fascinated and listened to it for a moment.

He then adjusted the instrument, walking away from the table wondering about the sounds he had heard. Other work occupied his time for the rest of the day and he soon put the episode out of his mind. That night, sitting in the dimly lighted laboratory, Edison thought of the repeater's strange action. The noise from it had seemed almost human in pitch, like a voice running at top speed. He mulled over the phenomenon, then finally locked the laboratory doors and returned home for a good night's rest.

It was now August and the heat was overbearing. Most of the men tucked handkerchiefs around their throats to absorb perspiration; some days hardly a waft of breeze could be felt, causing the laboratory thermometer to climb. It was on such a day that Edison summoned his machinist, John Kruesi, to his little office. The inventor looked up, handing him a sketch.

"Here, Kruesi," he said, "make this up right away."

The bearded machinist looked at the drawing and shook his head. It called for a metal cylinder mounted on a shaft; the shaft, in turn, was upheld by two metal supports on a platform. At the end of the shaft was a crank handle. Kruesi was used to making things with wires or switches, but this strange-looking instrument had none; as a matter of fact, it called for a mounted diaphragm with a blunt needle set in the center of it. An odd-looking thing, Kruesi thought. He peered at the illustration a moment longer, shaking his head. Edison laughed.

"The machine must talk, Kruesi," remarked the inventor.

The faithful machinist shook his head doubtfully, leaving the office with a grunt. He went directly to the shop and began work on the unusual creation his boss had thought up. Machines, he

The original phonograph of 1877

mulled, just do not speak — it was an impossibility. The heat must have affected Mr. Edison.

After a short period of time, Kruesi mounted the steps to the second floor of the laboratory. He carefully held the new machine in his arms. The workmen hesitated in their work, looking at the strange contraption. Edison ordered the machinist to set it on a table at the far end of the building, then asked for a sheet of tin foil. When it arrived, he carefully wrapped the foil about the instrument's metal cylinder and placed the diaphragm needle against it.

By this time, the staff had left their work and gathered about Edison. He looked at them in silence, then slowly began to turn the crank which revolved the cylinder. Suddenly, the foil ripped as the needle touched its surface. The men winked and nudged one another, feeling that the invention was a failure. Edison said nothing and again wound a sheet of foil about the grooved cylinder. Once again, he turned the crank slowly. This time the foil remained intact as the crude needle glided across its surface. The young inventor leaned over and began to shout into the mouthpiece, his voice loud and clear.

"Mary had a little lamb its fleece was white as snow and everywhere that Mary went the lamb was sure to go. How do you get that now? Hello! Hello!"

The room was silent as a tomb after this brief recitation. All eyes were upon him as he returned the cylinder to its original starting place. With a brief glance at the staff, he slowly began to turn the crank. Then, as though it was a voice from the grave, the machine began to talk.

"Mary had a little lamb its fleece was white as snow . . ." It was the voice of Edison, wobbly and blurred somewhat, but clear enough to distinguish the words. A shout went up from the men and they crowded even closer to their boss, slapping him on the back and yelling congratulations. Edison waved aside their praise.

"It was there all the time," he said, "we just had to look for it."

Mary had a little lamb its fleece was white as snow and everywhere that Mary went the lamb was sure to go. How do you get that now? Hello! Hello!

Thomas A. Edison

Edison's handwritten record of the first words he spoke into the phonograph

For most of the night, the men stayed on at the laboratory, whistling and reciting into the new phonograph. It was a modern miracle and, like most miracles, had come along at the right time. Operating funds had run quite low during the past months and Edison needed more capital. The phonograph would bring a great deal of money into the till, enabling the inventor to continue operation. Soon news of the phonograph traveled over the telegraph wires to New York City. The response was tremendous and it was no time until reporters besieged Edison at his laboratory. One day, a reporter from the "New York World" traveled to Menlo Park to obtain an interview concerning the miraculous phonograph. He asked Edison many questions about his creation, then inquired as to what sort of things were to be recorded on the machine. The young inventor answered without hesitation.

"Music, novels, general literature," he said. "Take music to begin with. We shall make phonograph records of orchestral concerts, brass and string bands, instrumental and vocal solos and part songs. The sheets bearing the sound impressions of this music will be removed from the phonograph and multiplied to any extent by electrotyping, and persons can make selections of any compositions they desire. This music may then be reproduced by any phonograph with the original sweetness and expression. And not only that, but the pitch can be raised or lowered by increasing or diminishing the speed of the phonograph."

"What will such a sheet of music cost?" asked the fascinated reporter.

"About twenty-five cents."

"But how can you record an orchestra, since it is necessary in talking to the phonograph to apply your mouth close to the diaphragm?"

Edison replied with apparent authority. "The phonograph will be attached to a hole in one end of a barrel, and from the other end will project a funnel like those used in ventilating steamships. This will receive the music from the entire orchestra, not of course reproducing it with so great a volume. Piano music will be caught by a hood placed over the instrument, the volume of the reproduction being one fourth that of the piano."

The reporter nodded in understanding, then continued with another question.

"What method will be pursued with literary matter?" he asked.

Edison again replied promptly. "We estimate that an ordinary fifty cent novel can be contained on this."

He paused to show the reporter a recording cylinder, then continued with enthusiasm.

"Novels and valuable literature will be read to the phonograph by elocutionists and persons understanding the subjects presented, and the matter will be multiplied by electrotyping in the same manner as music. You see, therefore, that you may have a phonograph in your parlors with an album of selected phonographic matter lying beside it. You may take a sheet from the album, place it on the phonograph, start the clock work and have a symphony. Then by changing the sheet you may listen to a chapter or two from a favorite novel. This may be followed by a song, a duet or a quartette. You can easily see what an advantage the phonograph will be to the blind, and, indeed, I have already received one hundred orders from such persons."

The reporter was amazed as he asked a final question.

"What will be the cost of a phonograph?"

"About a hundred dollars," replied the youthful inventor. "The instrument will be finished in all styles and handsomely decorated."

When the interview appeared in the pages of the "New York World," Edison was extremely pleased. Such stories would promote interest and sales of the phonograph, thus increasing a weak bank balance. A month later, the inventor took one of the machines with him and traveled to the New York office of the "Scientific American." Here, and with a great display, Edison demonstrated the talking instrument to the editors. On December 22, 1877, the magazine carried a brilliant account of the visit and the accomplishments of the phonograph.

"Mr. Thomas A. Edison," it read, "recently came into this office, placed a little machine on our desk, turned a crank, and the machine inquired as to our health, asked how we liked the phonograph, informed us that *it* was very well, and bade us a cordial good-night. These remarks were not only perfectly audible to ourselves, but to a dozen or more persons gathered around; and they were produced by the aid of no other mechanism than the simple little contrivance."

The article then went into detail as to the workings of the phonograph, but concluded with this wondrous prediction:

"We have already pointed out the startling possibility of the voices of the dead being reheard through this device, and there is no doubt but that its capabilities are fully equal to other results just as astonishing. When it becomes possible, as it doubtless will, to magnify the sound, the voices of such singers as Parepa and Titiens will not die with them, but will remain as long as the metal in which they may be embodied will last . . . It is already possible by ingenious optical contrivances to throw stereoscopic photographs of people on screens in full view of an audience. Add the talking phonograph to counterfeit their voices, and it would be difficult to carry the illusion of real presence much further."

Thus the article was concluded and for the first time, its printed prophecies reached the attention of scientists all over America.

About the same time Edison gave birth to the phonograph, his wife gave birth to their first child — a bright-eyed baby girl, named Marion. Her parents, of course, showered her with love and attention. Edison naturally thought of capturing the baby's cries on the new phonograph and made several desperate attempts. An amusing report of this project appeared in the "New York Herald."

"The most picturesque thing about the baby's utterances," stated the article, "was its crying, and the record of this its fond father determined to secure. How it would entertain him in his old age, he thought, to start the phonograph a-going and hear

Edison with an improved model of the phonograph in 1878

again the baby wails of his firstborn! So one afternoon Mr. Edison tore himself away from his work and climbed the big hill leading to his house. He went in a great hurry, for he is a man who grudges every working moment from his labors. A workman followed at his heels, carrying the only phonograph that at that time had been sufficiently completed to accomplish really good results.

"Reaching home and the nursery, Mr. Edison started the phonograph and brought the baby in front of it. But the baby didn't cry. Mr. Edison tumbled the youngster about, and rumpled its hair and did all sorts of things, but still the baby didn't cry. Then the inventor made dreadful faces, but the baby thought they were very funny, and crowed lustily. So back to the laboratory went Mr. Edison in a very unpleasant frame of mind, for the baby's untimely good humor had cost him an hour of work. The phonograph was also taken back.

"But he didn't give it up. The next afternoon he went home again, and the phonograph with him. But if the baby was good-natured the day before, this time it was absolutely cherubic. There was nothing at all that its father could do that didn't make the baby laugh. So back to work the inventor went again with a temper positively ruffled. The next day and the next he tried it, but all to no purpose.

"So at length, after much thought, he made a mighty resolve. It took a vast amount of determination on his part to screw his courage to the point of committing the awful deed, but he succeeded at last, and one morning, when he knew his wife was down town, he went quietly home with the phonograph and stole into the nursery, where the baby greeted him with its customary glee.

"Starting the machine, Mr. Edison ordered the nurse to leave the room. Then he took the baby on his knee and bared its chubby little leg. He took the tender flesh between his thumb and finger, clenched his teeth, shut his eyes tight, and made ready to — yes, actually to pinch the baby's leg. But just at the fateful moment the nurse peeped through the door, and, perceiving the horrid plot, flounced in and rescued the baby in the nick of time. Mr. Edison breathed a mighty sigh of relief as he gathered up the phonograph and went back to the laboratory. He then gave up the project of phonographing the baby's crying.

"But not long afterwards he accomplished his purpose in spite of everything, and quite unexpectedly, too. As soon as the baby was old enough to take notice, its mother took it down to the laboratory one sunny day, and when the big machinery was started a-roaring, the baby screwed up its face, opened its mouth, and emitted a series of woeful screams that made Mr. Edison leap to his feet. 'Stop the machinery and start the phonograph,' he shouted, and the record of his baby's crying was there and then accomplished."

The dream-like remembrance of the baby's crying returned to the old man slumped in his chair. He waked with a start, finding himself surrounded by the furnishings of his West Orange laboratory. He rubbed his eyes as if returning from a long sleep. Not having a watch, it was difficult to know how long he had napped. The aged inventor got to his feet and stretched slowly. Even now, the recollection of those faded Menlo Park days seemed quite real, almost as though the phonograph had been invented yesterday.

He thought for a moment of John Kruesi and of the faint recording he owned of his voice. Many times Edison would go to the vault to get the disc bearing the dead Kruesi's shadowy message; he would place it on the phonograph and with misty eyes, listen to his old employee talk. It made the past seem not so far away to the old man.

As he thought of Kruesi and the other boys at Menlo Park, a loud knock came at the door. It would be Meadowcroft, thought Edison, as he shuffled over to open it. Sure enough, in rushed the faithful secretary to thrust a batch of envelopes toward the inventor.

"Here is the mail," he shouted, placing it in Edison's wrinkled hand.

The old man thanked Meadowcroft in a loud reply and began

reading the many letters. After a moment, he paused, referring to one letter in particular.

"Here's a note from Francis Jehl," he exclaimed. "He might come to West Orange and pay me a visit. What a delight!"

The faithful secretary nodded in agreement. It had been a long time since they had seen Jehl and he knew a visit would please Mr. Edison. Meadowcroft lingered but a brief moment, then left the laboratory as quickly as he had entered it.

Edison returned to his chair, rereading the letter from Jehl. He shook his white head. Francis . . . good old Francis. He was now the only survivor of the Menlo Park staff who had worked on the electric light with Edison. What times they had experienced way back there in the laboratory. It seemed like only yesterday when Edison interviewed the young Jehl. Shortly before the boy's employment, Edison had announced that he was starting his search for the first successful electric light. Because of this, it had been a particularly busy day at the laboratory and the young man from New York could not have picked a worse time to call on the inventor.

Edison now chuckled as he thought of Francis Jehl, anxious and somewhat nervous, awaiting an interview with the Wizard of Menlo Park. To the old man, peering once again at the handwritten letter, the memory of that afternoon in 1878 came back vividly.

In reflection, the Menlo Park laboratory clock had just chimed when Edison looked up to find a young stranger standing before him.

It was Francis Jehl . . . and the beginning of an association which would span the next fifty-three years. Once again, in the aged memory of the old inventor, the Menlo Park of 1878 had come back to life.

From an old photograph

Francis Jehl, Edison's assistant, during his Menlo Park days

(Photograph originally presented to the author by Mrs. Francis Jehl)

Defeat Of Darkness

THE ECHO OF THE Seth Thomas clock still lingered in the room. Its quiet chiming went unnoticed by Edison who sat working at the south end of the laboratory. He was deeply engrossed in the performance of an experimental platinum lamp. For a long time, he tinkered with it before noticing the young man. At last, he lifted his eyes from the lamp to meet the steady — and admiring — gaze of Francis Jehl. The inventor frowned, then smiled broadly.

"Hello," he said, "what do you want?"

The young man clutched a derby hat in his hands, nervously twisting it. To him, Thomas Edison was one of the greatest men of all time. It was almost unbelievable to be standing here in his famous laboratory and to be actually speaking with him. Jehl shifted slightly, then modestly answered the waiting Edison.

"I have a letter of introduction," he said and stepped over to hand it to the young inventor.

It was a brief note from Grosvenor P. Lowrey, general counsel for Western Union and a friend of Edison's. Young Jehl had worked in the New York office of Western Union and it was there that he expressed a desire to work for Edison. The kind Lowrey, willing to help the lad, promised a letter of introduction and had promptly written it.

Standing now in the Menlo Park laboratory, Francis Jehl felt deep gratitude toward his former employer. This was the chance of a lifetime and his excitement was unbounded. The quick eyes of Edison read the note, pausing to look into Jehl's eager face.

"Can you start now?" asked the inventor.

Francis Jehl nodded with enthusiasm.

"Yes, sir," he replied, still twisting the derby in his hands.

Edison turned toward the south end of the laboratory.

"See that table yonder? I would like for you to clean the wet batteries. We need them for some work tonight."

Jehl nodded promptly in response to the request. He was familiar with the Bunsen batteries and knew exactly how to clean them. With deft movements, the young man removed his coat and placed it on a chair, along with the smartly styled hat. He rolled up his shirt sleeves and headed for the battery table. He was determined that his first chore for Edison be done with correctness and efficiency.

While the new employee plunged into the cleaning job, Edison returned to his work with the platinum lamp. It consisted of a glass cylinder mounted atop a wooden stand; inside the cylinder a coil of platinum was mounted and connected by wires to electric cells. When proper connection was made, the current caused the coil to heat to such intensity that after a moment, light glowed inside the cylinder. Too much current and the problem of oxygen in the air caused the coil to burn out almost immediately. Time after time, Edison had experimented with this type of lighting, only to end in failure. He was thoroughly familiar with the efforts of others to discover an electric light. Similar experiments had recently been conducted in England and Russia, but without definite success. For one thing — regardless of the type of lamp — it had to be cheap to operate, have no odor or flicker and be convenient to install. Edison now meditated on these problems, turning only once to glance at his new employee at the battery table.

Francis Jehl was scrubbing the glass jars with vigor. They fairly shone with brilliance as he polished them with a dry cloth. Edison nodded in pleasure. It looked as though the young man was industrious and would mix well with his other employees. The inventor thought of his men with pride. Each was an expert in his field and performed with faithfulness. There was Francis Upton, a brilliant mathematician; Charles Batchelor, an esteemed assistant to the inventor; John Kruesi, the able and deft mechanic; "Doc" Haid, the efficient laboratory chemist; and Stockton L. Griffin, private secretary to Edison. These were but a few of the Menlo Park staff who kept the laboratory humming with research and experimentation. Nowhere in the country was there a more cooperative work team than those Edison had assembled in his employ. And now, young Francis Jehl had joined the illustrious ranks.

Edison, seeing that dusk was setting in, got up from the worktable. He sauntered to Jehl's side, noticing that the batteries were cleaned and filled.

"You can have the rest of the day off," he suggested quietly.

Francis nodded in response, wiping his forehead with the cloth. Edison inspected his work and gave it his full approval. He then suggested that the boy go across the street to Sarah Jordan's boardinghouse and rent a room. It would be his home while at Menlo Park and the meals served there were excellent. Jehl thanked him for this advice and promptly put on his coat; the cleaning job had exercised his muscles and his stomach growled with hunger. Tired as he was, Francis was yet grateful to the inventor for this marvelous opportunity and once again expressed his thanks. Edison waved aside the boy's remarks and watched him leave for the first floor of the laboratory. He smiled to himself at Jehl's eagerness, then returned to the platinum lamp and the quest for electric light.

Downstairs, Jehl found the little business office in a state of confusion. Books were stacked on the floor and papers were scattered everywhere. He was informed by a worker that this had been moving day.

"Moved into the new brick office and library," he snapped. "Sure is a beauty, isn't it?"

Jehl nodded in agreement and stepped out on the front porch of the laboratory. The library was situated to the left and boasted two well furnished floors. Through the windows, Jehl could

Edison's Menlo Park library and office building

(As restored at Henry Ford's Greenfield Village, Dearborn, Michigan)

see the flickering of gas lamps and the hurried activity of Mr. Griffin, Edison's secretary. Truly, this would be a wonderland of research and Jehl longed for a chance to visit the new library with its shelves of technical books. He then bade his fellow worker good night and headed for Mrs. Jordan's boardinghouse, still looking back at the new brick building.

Mrs. Sarah Jordan proved to be a kindly woman. Her boardinghouse was neat and the parlor boasted an atmosphere of warmth and welcome. She discussed terms with young Jehl and, after reaching a quick financial agreement, showed him to his room. It was small, but neatly and modestly furnished. A bed with a soft coverlet dominated the room with a feeling of serene comfort. Dainty fresh curtains hung at the windows and the washstand boasted a delicately painted bowl and water pitcher. Jehl was delighted with his new home and hummed happily as Mrs. Jordan promptly retreated to the lower floor and her kitchen.

Jehl carefully unpacked his few belongings, placing them in a wooden bureau. He glanced with pride at a copy of an electrical testing handbook given him by Mr. Lowrey. Thanks to that good man, he was now a member of the Edison team and faced a promising future. He tenderly laid the book on a night stand and then washed up for supper.

Almost immediately, Mrs. Jordan summoned her boarders to the evening meal. Jehl found not only the food, but the company quite excellent. A few of the laboratory men also boarded here and they chatted words of welcome to the young man. He responded with thankfulness and, after a warm and filling meal, waved them good evening. Later that night, tucked in his snug bed, Francis Jehl thought of Edison's laboratory and the great man's work there. His heart still pounded with excitement until finally, lulled by hopeful dreams of the days to come, he fell into a deep and restful slumber.

His adventures at Menlo Park had just begun.

The next morning dawned dark and rainy. The laboratory was

Sarah Jordan's boardinghouse at Menlo Park

(As restored at Henry Ford's Greenfield Village, Dearborn, Michigan)

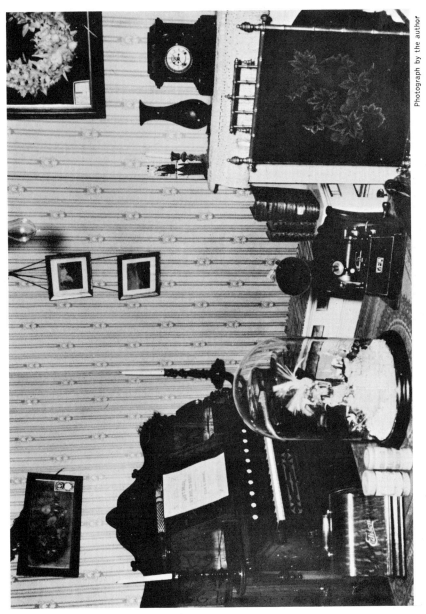

The parlor of Sarah Jordan's boardinghouse

(As restored at Henry Ford's Greenfield Village, Dearborn, Michigan)

a veritable hive of activity as young Jehl returned to work. The second floor of the long building was dotted with men busy at their separate tasks. Many of them Jehl had not met, but in no time he was introduced to them all: Charles L. Clarke . . . William Carman . . . Samuel Mott . . . George Dean . . . Charles Hughes . . . George Hill . . . John Lawson . . . George Carman . . . Charles Flammer . . . Ludwig Boehm . . . Charles Mott and last, but not least, a frequent visitor to the laboratory, J. U. Mackenzie, Edison's old telegraph instructor.

The gas lights burned brightly that morning, combating the darkness caused by the rain outside. The sounds of clicks, taps and grinding filled the laboratory as the staff began their day's work. Jehl was promptly given an assignment and found himself quietly laboring beside his co-workers. Edison meanwhile continued his tinkering with the platinum lamp, occasionally calling Batchelor to his side for consultation. The bearded assistant would bend his head close to his chief's as they examined the results of an experiment together.

Edison felt that pressure was on him to find the electric light. Because of his announcement that he would find the light, every scientific eye was focused on Menlo Park. Luckily, several prominent businessmen from New York had given Edison funds with which to work; these men, including J. P. Morgan, Henry Villard and Grosvenor Lowrey, had faith in his ability and felt that their investment was secure. The moment the inventor mentioned his search for the light, gas stocks fell off and raised the ire of the gas industry. Now, after months of searching, Edison was still unsuccessful.

His critics began to nag at him and used the press to indicate their feelings. In the "Scientific American" there appeared such an article on February 15, 1879. It was brief, but to the point.

"The Philadelphia Bulletin," it read, "suggests that if Mr. Edison wishes public faith in that electric light of his to remain steadfast, he will have to give an early demonstration of the truth of his claim that it is a practical success. When he first announced that he had solved the problem of dividing the light and of adapting it to domestic uses, there was a very general inclination to accept the story with absolute confidence because Mr. Edison had proved by his previous inventions that he could achieve some things which had been regarded by other men as impossible. But, after all, the proof of the pudding is in the eating, and the world, after waiting patiently for the public display of an invention which sent gas stocks down as soon as it was heralded, will be disposed, unless Mr. Edison shows his hand, to suspect that the Edison Electric Light and the Keely Motor will have to be ranked together as enterprises which contained more of promise than of performance."

Such reports as these, coupled with mouth-to-mouth rumors, pricked Edison's anger. He labored continuously now in his determined search and tried to ignore the critics' bitter remarks. Experiment after experiment was performed and each failure noted in the laboratory notebooks. Metals of all sorts were used as sources of possible lighting, but none seemed as good as platinum; even this lamp, patented by Edison in April, was not truly a success.

In his twilight years, as the dean of American inventors, the white-headed Edison would remember these days of bitter criticism.

"Grouches," he would shout, "are nearly always pinheads, small men who have never made any effort to improve their mental capacity."

The wrinkled old hand would pound a table top as he recalled the trying months spent in search of his electric light. At times, it seemed so long ago to the elderly inventor that he forgave the harsh attacks upon his work. But to the younger man, in the year 1879, the research and experimentation on the lamp were of utmost urgency. His critics continued to scorn his efforts and create doubt in the public's mind as to Edison's ability.

Every member of the staff at Menlo Park was influenced by their chief's zeal. They ate, slept and talked the electric light; they labored untold hours in the hope of coming up with new ideas or theories; their families came to consider them as almost strangers, due to their excessive hours away from home. And worse, it seemed at times that the search might end in total failure.

Edison studied the platinum lamp with intensity. He knew that the overabundance of oxygen was causing the lamp to burn out. If there was some way of protecting the wire coil from the air, then there might be a chance of its burning longer. This particular morning, as the rain fell mournfully outside, Edison told Batchelor about his oxygen theory. The two men chatted for a few moments until the inventor rose to his feet as though struck by lightning.

"Batch," he exclaimed, "I may have an idea. We're getting nowhere as long as the platinum coil is exposed to the air. Too much oxygen."

He paused, running a hand through his bushy hair, as he was prone to do when thinking. Batchelor stood silently as his chief turned an idea over in his mind. Suddenly, Edison slapped his knee.

"Let's try our vacuum pump on it," he said. "If we can drain off as much oxygen as possible, it'll probably burn longer."

Batchelor nodded in agreement, then left to get the pump. Edison stood silent until his assistant, puffing with exertion, returned with the equipment. It consisted of an elevated platform, much like a cake dish, with a glass dome over it. A pump handle was attached to the machine, and, when pumped up and down, it withdrew air from the glass. Edison promptly called for another metal coil and connected it to the wires jutting from the pump base; the glass housing was placed over it and the unit was ready for operation.

Edison looked up and called for Francis Jehl. The young man, laying aside his work, rushed to the worktable. His employer nodded toward the vacuum pump.

"Francis, take hold of that handle and start pumping," he ordered. "We've got to get as much vacuum in that glass as we can."

Jehl grasped the two ends of the pump handle and began to move them up and down. Over and over again, he repeated this action, never once hesitating as he did so. The other workmen gathered about the table, their eyes fastened upon the glass dome. Edison stood quietly while Jehl continued pumping slowly. Finally, when it seemed that no more air could be withdrawn from the dome, Edison called for a halt.

The men moved in even closer now, anxious to see what might happen. There was a strained silence in the room as Edison connected the wires to the batteries which rested beside the pump. Slowly, the metal coil began to redden with electrical heat; it grew brighter and brighter until, in a few moments, it glowed with light. This time, it did not burn out immediately, but continued glowing like a reddened coal. Several minutes passed until finally, breaking the silence, Edison issued an order.

"Francis, keep pumping. Make sure you've gotten as much of that air out as possible."

The young assistant pumped laboriously, while beads of sweat dropped from his forehead. The other workmen said nothing as the glass was being drained of more air. Finally, after several moments, Edison ordered Jehl to cease pumping. He peered intently at the glimmering coil which seemed even brighter than before.

"That's the answer," the inventor whispered, "a vacuum will do the trick."

He watched the soft light with deep absorption until finally, with a sudden burst, it burned out. A low murmur went up from the little group at the table. Edison did not move, but stood quietly beside the pump.

"Not enough vacuum," he remarked and walked away to the south end of the laboratory.

After this episode, the men made certain he was not disturbed. They knew that their chief was deep in meditation and wished to be alone. Because of their respect, each of them returned to his work in complete silence.

In the days to come, Edison pondered the problem of air and oxygen effects. He was certain that if all of the oxygen was removed from a glass container, the element inside might burn indefinitely. From that time on, he began to experiment with hundreds of metals, but with little or no success. Before he realized it, thirteen months had dragged by without results.

It was now October of 1879. His financial backers had become alarmed that their faith in him had not reaped dividends. They continuously inquired as to his progress and he repeatedly reported no results. Edison had meanwhile sent over to Princeton University for a Sprengel vacuum pump; it was, as far as he knew, the only efficient vacuum instrument in the country. The pump resembled an upright board with glass tubing wandering over the face of it. Mercury was poured into glass tubing at the top of the board; as the mercury flowed downward, it created a vacuum by pushing air ahead of it. On an extension arm of the pump was a connection for Edison's glass bulbs. In these bulbs he placed experimental filaments and once a good vacuum was achieved, he tested them.

The filaments failed one after another. Even mounting them in a glass globe resulted in disaster, for some filaments were too fine and shattered to pieces. On other heartbreaking occasions, the glass would break before it was placed on the pump and the work had to be done over. Hours of testing brought less hope as he conducted more and more experiments.

One night, after a day of fruitless testing, Edison stayed late at the laboratory. He sat behind a huge chest of drawers near the south end of the room. Before him, on the top of the stained chest, was a mortar and pestle used in grinding compounds; beside it lay a carbon mixture which had been used during the development of the telephone transmitter. As Edison sat in meditation, his fingers toyed with a piece of the sticky carbon; he absently rolled it into a fine string as he mulled over the problems facing him. The dim light from the gas jets overhead cast shadows upon the inventor's face. He sat for a long time, completely oblivious to the stringy black carbon in his hand. In a moment, he glanced down at the rope-like compound and stared at it. Suddenly, he sat up with almost alarm.

Carbon! Why had he not thought of carbon? Surely it would resist electricity to the point of illumination, particularly in a glass of vacuum. He jumped to his feet and started for the stairs, but stopped. It was too late tonight to make a carbon filament and besides, the men were at home and sound asleep. He would wait until the next morning. For a long while, he lingered in the laboratory, still toying with the carbon in his hand. At last a ray of hope had filtered through his defeats. After nine thousand separate experiments for a filament, this might be the answer. With almost joy in his heart, he locked the laboratory doors and walked through the night, impatient for dawn.

The next day, Edison rushed to the laboratory in great haste. Immediately, he asked Batchelor to fetch him a spool of sewing thread and bring it to the chest of drawers. When the thread arrived, Edison sat down and quickly prepared a black carbon paste. He then took a short length of thread and impregnated it with the sticky compound; he carefully rolled it over and over until the thread was entirely covered with carbon. With deft hands, Edison then fashioned the material into a horseshoe shape and gently handed it to Batchelor.

Many years later, enthroned in his West Orange laboratory, the aging Edison would recall the story of that thread filament. His old eyes gleamed with excitement as he related the events that transpired.

"We had to take this piece of carbonized thread," he mused, "to the glass-blower's house. With the utmost precaution Batchelor took up the precious carbon, and I marched after him, as if guarding a mighty treasure. To our consternation, just as we reached the glass-blower's bench the wretched carbon broke. We turned back to the main laboratory and set to work again. It was late in the afternoon before we had produced another carbon, which was again broken by a jeweler's screwdriver falling against it. But we turned back again, and before night the carbon was completed."

The bulb was tenderly carried upstairs and placed on the Sprengel pump. Francis Jehl mounted a short wooden step and began, at Edison's instruction, to pour mercury into the pump's tubing. Minutes passed as a vacuum was created in the shiny

Edison's Menlo Park machine shop and glass blower's house

(As restored at Henry Ford's Greenfield Village, Dearborn, Michigan)

glass globe. Silence reigned in the room as every eye rested upon the thin filament. Finally the proper vacuum was achieved and Edison stepped up to the pump.

His fingers moved toward the electrical switch which rested on the worktable. Slowly, he threw the switch and gazed at the globe. Of a sudden the carbonized thread came brilliantly alive with light. Its glare was dazzling and was almost blinding in its intensity. A shout went up from the men as they squinted at the lamp, their excitement uncontrollable. Edison sat down in his chair beside the pump and watched the bulb in complete silence. It continued to burn brightly and steadily, without any flickering. For the next few hours, it blazed like a star and never once faltered. The men came and went, checking their watches and shaking puzzled heads. They had almost become accustomed to failure and it was with some skepticism that they watched the lamp.

Many years later, the wise old inventor would speak of that day in his own words. His chin sagged in remembrance at the thought of the miraculous invention.

"The day was — let me see — October 21, 1879. We sat and looked, and the lamp continued to burn, and the longer it burned, the more fascinated we were. None of us could go to bed — there was no sleep for any of us for forty hours. We sat and just watched it with anxiety growing into elation. It lasted about forty-five hours."

That first memorable night was a vigil of hope and endurance. Most of the workmen came and went, anxious to see how long the lamp might burn. Francis Jehl stayed at Edison's side constantly while his chief sat observing the light. The night seemed quite long at times and, aside from talking, there was little to do. A warm snack supper was sent up for Edison and the young assistant; this was devoured with gusto and followed by a short nap. Afterward, Jehl went to a workbench and looked at his personal drafting set. It was neatly housed in a long black box from which he removed each instrument and buffed it with a dry cloth. When satisfied that the kit was in order, he placed it once again on the table and returned to Edison.

Edison studies the electric lamp

The inventor talked of many things that night. He stretched, yawned and walked about the laboratory for exercise. Jehl knew how much the discovery of the lamp meant to his chief and he was grateful for this time with him. This was an earth-shaking event and to be a part of it was unforgettable. Francis reminded himself to let Mr. Lowrey know how much he appreciated this new job; surely the former employer would like to know that the young man's future looked bright.

Edison finally got up out of his chair, glancing at the Seth Thomas clock. He nodded to his new assistant and pointed to the face of the clock.

"Forty-five hours," he commented. "Let's see what the light can really do."

By this time, several of the men had returned to the second floor of the laboratory. They stood close to their chief as he checked the battery supply. He looked about him, then winked slyly.

"Give her more juice," he ordered. "So far it's gone to about twenty-five candle power without melting. Let's find out how much more it'll take."

After connecting additional power to the lamp, he stood watching intently. The filament burned with even greater intensity until, quicker than the blink of an eye, it burned out. A gasp went up from the onlookers as the glass bulb darkened. Edison shook his head enthusiastically.

"If it will burn that number of hours now," he exclaimed, "I know I can make it burn a hundred hours."

The rest of that day he gave a great deal of thought to the filament of thread. It had been satisfactory, but he hoped to find an even more practical material for the lamp. Several days later, after a thorough investigation, he decided to use cardboard for the filaments, making them in a horseshoe pattern like the sewing thread. When placed on the vacuum pump, these proved successful and Edison ordered that several of them be made up immediately.

He called his entire staff together and informed them that he

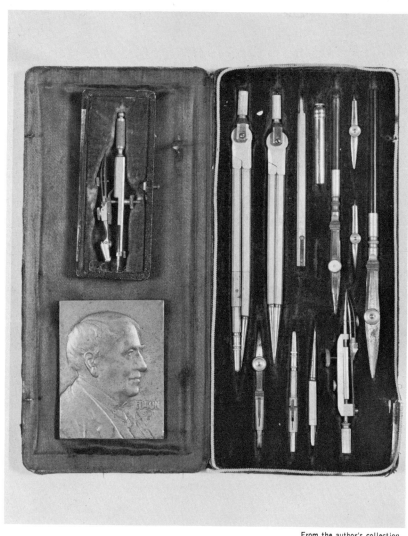

Drafting set used by Francis Jehl at Menlo Park in 1879

(Originally presented to the author by Mrs. Francis Jehl)

planned a public demonstration of the new lamp. First, a great deal of work and research must be done in preparation. A dynamo and generator must be designed to create the amount of electricity needed to light Menlo Park; the original gas jets in the buildings were to be used as electrical lighting fixtures, as well as the lamp posts outside the laboratory and down Christie Street. Even Mrs. Jordan's boardinghouse and Charles Batchelor's dwelling, as well as the inventor's own home, would be lighted.

As the men listened to his intense plans, they shook doubtful heads. It seemed to be a tremendous task and none of them knew much about this new field. Surely they could not be prepared any time soon for such a display. Edison showed no alarm whatsoever, but kept on talking rapidly of the things which must be done.

"But this is October," exclaimed one of the men. "When do you plan this show for the public?"

Edison stared out the laboratory window for a moment. His hand brushed through the bushy head of hair until finally, with a smile, he answered.

"By New Year's Eve, gentlemen," he said. "New Year's Eve — right here in Menlo Park."

With that, he turned from the group and descended the stairs. The men stood in utter amazement, unable to believe that such a miracle could be accomplished in two months. Surely, their chief would allow them more time than that. They stood chattering for several minutes until the laboratory clock chimed the hour. It was but a reminder of how little time remained to glorify Menlo Park in a blanket of blazing light.

Thomas Edison had dispelled the darkness of night. It was now up to them to help him light the world.

Edison's first commercial lamp

The Illustrious Illuminator

MORE THAN FIFTY years had now passed since the invention of the electric light. To the aged inventor, sitting in his West Orange laboratory, it seemed like only yesterday. As the wrinkled hand turned the pages of Francis Jehl's letter, the old man smiled to himself. Through the mist of the past, he could recall the hurried activities at Menlo Park in preparation for the lighting demonstration. What excitement there had been — what hustling had gone on for a full two months. The old inventor, touched by the onslaught of feebleness, slowly got up from his chair. He quietly walked to a table and opened a worn drawer. From its musty interior, he retrieved a yellowed newspaper, its folds torn and stained. This had been one of the first printed articles telling of the new electric light.

As the old man's eyes scanned the text, he was struck with sentimental nostalgia. The years seemed again to wash away, leaving only yesterday bright and alive. In remembrance, he was miles away from West Orange, living once more those wonderful days of 1879. The sound of old Charles Batchelor's voice floated to him from the vastness of the past. It was loud and clear as, in memory, the faithful associate dashed up the stairs of the Menlo Park laboratory. Yes, it was 1879 again and Edison was planning for his lighting demonstration.

"Chief! Chief!" The voice shouted down through the years.

It was Batchelor excitedly waving a newspaper in his hand. Edison, working on a technical layout for a new generator, looked up in wonderment.

"What in the world is the matter, Batch? Has something gone wrong downstairs?"

"The New York Herald's" account of Edison's
discovery of the electric light

The winded assistant rushed to his chief's side. His face was pink from running.

"Everything's all right," he puffed. "I just got this copy of the 'New York Herald.' There's a story on the light. I think you ought to read it."

Edison threw down his pencil, quite upset. He had not planned for any news to be given to the public yet. When he had first announced the success of the light over the telegraph, he felt that would be sufficient. He quickly snatched the newspaper from Batchelor's hand. It was dated December 21, 1879. His eyes hurriedly scanned the boldly printed headlines.

"EDISON'S LIGHT . . . The Great Inventor's Triumph In Electric Illumination . . . A Scrap of Paper . . . It Makes a Light, Without Gas or Flame, Cheaper Than Oil . . . SUCCESS IN A COTTON THREAD."

Edison's brows knitted together in displeasure. He recalled the recent visit of the "Herald" reporter and how he had given him information about the light; their agreement, however, was for the newspaper not to release a story until a specified date. Now they had violated the agreement with this premature article. Edison, filled with disgust, continued reading the article.

"The near approach of the first public exhibition of Edison's long looked for electric light, announced to take place on New Year's Eve at Menlo Park, on which occasion that place will be illuminated with the new light, has revived public interest in the great inventor's work, and throughout the civilized world scientists and people generally are anxiously awaiting the result. From the beginning of his experiments in electric lighting to the present time, Mr. Edison has kept his laboratory guardedly closed, and no authoritative account (except that published in the 'Herald' some months ago relating to his first patent) of any of the important steps of his progress has been made public — a course of procedure the inventor found absolutely necessary for his own protection. The 'Herald' is now, however, enabled to present to its readers a full and accurate account of his work from its inception to its completion.

"Edison's electric light, incredible as it may appear, is produced from a little piece of paper — a tiny strip of paper that a breath would blow away. Through this little strip of paper is passed an electric current, and the result is a bright, beautiful light, like the mellow sunset of an Italian autumn.

" 'But paper instantly burns, even under the trifling heat of a tallow candle!' exclaims the sceptic, 'and how, then, can it withstand the fierce heat of an electric current.' Very true, but Edison makes the little piece of paper more infusible than platinum, more durable than granite. And this involves no complicated process. The paper is merely baked in an oven until all its elements have passed away except its carbon framework. The latter is then placed in a glass globe connected with the wires leading to the electricity producing machine, and the air exhausted from the globe. Then the apparatus is ready to give out a light that produces no deleterious gases, no smoke, no offensive odors — a light without flame, without danger, requiring no matches to ignite, giving out but little heat, vitiating no air, and free from all flickering; a light that is a little globe of sunshine, a veritable Aladdin's lamp. And this light, the inventor claims, can be produced cheaper than that from the cheapest oil.

"Were it not for the phonograph, the quadruplex telegraph, the telephone and the various other remarkable productions of the great inventor the world might well hesitate to accept his assurance that such a beneficent result had been obtained, but, as it is, his past achievements in science are sufficient guarantee that his claims are not without foundation, even though for months past the press of Europe and America has teemed with dissertations and expositions from learned scientists ridiculing Edison and showing that it was impossible for him to achieve that which he has undertaken.

"Before concluding this article it is only proper that due credit should be given to those whose untiring energy and skilled handicraft made possible the perfection of the great inventor's system — viz., his chief laboratory assistants: for, although Edison's was the mind that originated all, theirs were the hands that deftly carried out his wishes. Principal among his assistants, and so intimately associated with him in his work that his absence from the laboratory is invariably a signal for Mr. Edison to suspend labor, is Mr. Charles Batchelor. For the past eight years Mr. Batchelor has worked side by side with the inventor, carrying out his plans with rare ability, and to his energy and skill is due not a little. Next come Messrs. Upton and Kruesi, both heads of departments, the one attending to the fine electrical work and the other to the mechanical details of the machine department. Among the others whose ability has helped to contribute to the inventor's great success, each in his particular sphere, are Mr. Griffin, Mr. Carman, Mr. Jehl, Mr. Force and Mr. Boehm."

When he had finished reading the article, Edison threw the newspaper on the floor. His brows were gathered in a frown.

"What nerve!" he exclaimed. "That reporter knew how I felt about printing this. Now everyone will bother us for more news."

Batchelor did not respond, but waited for his chief to continue. He knew that at times like this, it was better to be silent. Edison suddenly stood up from his work, dropping a rule on the table.

"The article is accurate enough, but I wanted to wait until we'd lighted Menlo Park. Inform the staff that I don't want to be bothered with reporters. I'm too busy."

The loyal assistant nodded in understanding as Edison immediately returned to his work. The problem at hand — that of designing generators and dynamos — was a tremendous one and required his steady concentration. For the past several weeks he and all of the workmen had been feverishly occupied: stringing wires, mounting filaments, setting up lamp posts, winding coils and installing switches, reworking gas fixtures, designing lamp base mounts and checking the giant steam engine capacity. The days flew by as November surrendered to December and now, the last week of the year was upon them.

However, everything was soon in order and Menlo Park was prepared for the demonstration. Lights had been installed throughout the laboratory, machine shop and the new library; Christie

Courtesy Department of the Interior, National Park Service

Menlo Park as it appeared in the winter of 1879

Street was lined with lamp posts connected in a series by long bright copper wires; across the dirt road, Mrs. Jordan's boarding-house and Batchelor's residence had been the scene of busy activity also, with lighting facilities being installed. Edison's own home, down the hill, had been wired for the new electric lamps and stood waiting for the brilliant demonstration.

The public was notified prior to New Year's Eve that the exhibit was to take place. Special trains from New York were scheduled for the trip to Menlo Park and countless numbers of people made plans to go. Shortly before New Year's Eve, a gentle white snow had begun to fall and in no time, the laboratory and grounds were covered by a thick white blanket. The air was bitter cold and the shouts of workmen virtually froze in the winter air. Excitement ran high as the final touches were made prior to the exhibit. Edison and his entire staff found themselves dashing here and there in a state of frenzy, giving every piece of equipment a final check.

Edison decided at the last minute to give a few personal friends a preview of the electric lamp. Because of the crowds anticipated on New Year's Eve, he invited his close friends, and a few eager reporters, to visit Menlo Park the last few days of December. Now, because of two special showings, he hurried to prepare the buildings for the demonstration, calling on every hand available in order to be sufficiently ready.

Then time ran out — the last week of December arrived. Crowds journeyed by foot from the railway station up to the laboratory where they were met by a fairyland of light. The thick snow reflected the brilliance of the glowing glass globes in the lamp posts. The laboratory, looming boldly in the night, was ablaze with light and radiated a glow of welcome to the visitors. It was a sight never to be forgotten.

Edison, in his final years, stooped and white-haired, often thought of that long-ago night. His frail hands would shake as he read a reporter's faded account in an issue of the "Herald," dated 1879. It called to mind once again that glorious event and the excitement that prevailed.

"The laboratory of Mr. Edison at Menlo Park," said the article, "was brilliantly illuminated last night with the new electric light, the occasion being a visit of a number of the inventor's personal friends. Forty lamps in all were burning from six o'clock until after ten. The various parts of the system were explained by the inventor at length. As a practical illustration of his method of subdividing the electric current he had two copper wires of about an eighth of an inch in thickness leading to the generating machines placed side by side on cleats along tables nearly the entire length of the laboratory. To these he connected lamp after lamp by merely fastening little wires to each of the parallel supply wires and then attaching them to the lamps. The illumination or extinguishment made not the slightest perceptible difference in the strength of the current.

"Twenty electric lamps burned with exactly the same brilliancy as did one when the other nineteen were disconnected. The light given was of the brilliancy of the best gas jet, perhaps a trifle more brilliant. The effect of the light on the eyes was much superior to gas in softness and excited the admiration of all who saw it.

"A new feature, shown by the inventor for the first time, was the method of regulating the strength of the current to be used at the central stations. By moving a little wheel the assistant in charge of this branch of the system was enabled to readily vary the strength of the electric lights from the merest glimmer to a dazzling incandescence. When the latter point was reached the little horseshoe paper presented the appearance of a beautiful globe of fire. The method of obtaining the vacuum in the little glass bulbs of the lamps was also explained and proved highly interesting.

" 'Wonderful!' When you hear this word rolled out once in a while with the proper intensity of accent, as in the grand chorus of the 'Messiah,' it has a lifting effect upon the emotions. When you hear it three or four hundred times in a day it begins to lose force and you search about for synonyms. Out here at the home of the wizard in these times you listen to it from the lips of battalions of visitors, and you sympathize with the men of Athens who grew weary of hearing a great citizen called 'Aristides the Just.' All this while you are under the influence of the wonderful yourself. It is not only the little glowing globes hung here and there, but a thousand and one things appeal to your sense of admiration besides, above all of which towers, as the creator does above his creature, the man himself.

" 'It is not much of a place,' said a Philadelphia millionaire to a New York capitalist, yesterday, as they looked around at the dozen or so of houses that dot the otherwise bare hillside that is called Menlo Park. But few thought about such things, though the view across the pleasant, undulating country, now wrapped in a light garment of snow, with the brown skeletons of the woods breaking the sky line, is soothing and charming. All came with one passion — the electric light and its maker. They are of all classes, these visitors, of different degrees of wealth and importance in the community and varying degrees of scientific ignorance. Few, indeed, are they who can approximately measure what has been done in this matter, and still fewer those who, knowing its worth, admit it. But the homage of the mass to genius which they cannot comprehend makes up in quantity at any rate for any shortcomings in quality. It is a time of rapid conversions. The little horseshoe holds its own.

"Outside the building called the office, on two ordinary lamp-posts, gleamed, last evening, two little electric lamps. Afar off they seemed two large globes of fire. It was not till you came close by that you saw the little incandescent hoop of carbon held up by its delicate platinum clamps inside the small globe exhausted of air. In the office the lights were all electric. In the library upstairs it was the same. Over in the laboratory, upstairs and downstairs, it was the same. Such volleys of questions as were pouring out! Every assistant and even every boy was examined. All who came were satisfied. The visitors learned — for it was easy as Hamlet said lying was — to set the little carbon hoops alight by laying them down between the two wires on the main table. And Edison was there — a study to all, but divined by none.

By and by the visitors moved off, now stopping to look at the chalk telephone that speaks aloud. You hear of ohms and circuits, generators and so forth. They have been round the strange, complicated looking vacuum pumps, made out of glass tubing twisted up and twisted down.

"They have been down where the beardless boy with all the enthusiasm of an artist blows the lamps, seals in the thin wires and inserts the carbon hoop and leaves it all ready to be exhausted of air. There is a fascination about glass blowing, and this young Mr. Boehm, while a man in his business, is a child in his fancy, and he becomes as joyous over the delight of the onlookers as ever was a boy in a baseball field. He is a blue blood glass blower, and tells you his titles to skill with the conscious pride of a university graduate — for is he not a pupil of the late Dr. Geissler, whose fame is world-wide, but whose blowpipe is now laid away forever. The visitors have been around to see the engine, the generators, the regulators, the dynamometer. Satisfied about the electric light, they have asked about the tasimeter, the microphone, the phonograph and a dozen other things, as though they wanted to improve every instant before the train starts. At last they go in twos and threes down the hill to the railroad track, and it is all 'wonderful!' 'marvelous!' 'wonderful, wonderful!' among them till the train takes them away and Menlo Park is left to itself."

The elderly Edison smiled as he recollected these faraway memories. His old head shook with remembrance while he continued this exciting account of his exhibition. For the rest of his life, it would remain fresh and vivid, just as though it happened yesterday.

"It was quiet out here this morning and through the day as far as visitors were concerned. The machine shops were running full blast, and the laboratory was endued with its mysterious activity to the full. You would get the idea at first that in this place work was only taken up spasmodically, because you might see a man in broad daylight asleep on a bench, but shortly you discover that they only leave off work for short spells. Hence a peculiar

Bohemian air about the place and all who are in it that might be a sign of demoralization in any other establishment in the world.

"The afternoon trains brought some visitors, but in the evening every train set down a couple of score at least. All immediately started for the scene of the laboratory, and a good many of those simple people who hold that Rome was built in a day and those modest people who believe that the hinges of the universe should turn upon the pivot of their desires expressed disappointment that they did not step out of the train upon a scene from fairyland. The moon was obscured by clouds, the way was dark up the little plank road, and the new white lamp-posts seemed to be stretching up their long fingers to clutch a little light from the heavens since Edison would not give them any of his little horseshoes. In fact, as the inventor said to me today, he is only waiting for another electric generator to be finished to light up all these long white fellows in what is out of courtesy called a street. It will, he expects, be ready today, and tonight he hopes to have fifteen street lamps and several of the houses lighted up.

" 'It is a mistake to suppose,' said Edison, 'that a few lamps here or there over Menlo Park is all I want. I intend to make an actual test of my eighty horsepower engine and to put on every lamp it will run. I hope to have 800 of them. I shall put a dozen of them over there a mile away and turn them on and off from the window. I don't know where I'll put them all, unless along the fence. So everybody will have plenty of time to see them. It will take weeks to get them all out, though we are working night and day.'

"The stream of visitors passed through the shops, admired and wondered at the steady electric lights and called things by all sorts of laudatory epithets. Now and again a well-informed visitor would catch Mr. Batchelor or Mr. Upton and ply him with questions upon candle power, gas-jet power and kindred intricate matters that are 'caviare to the general.' A particular object of interest was the register for regulating the strength of the current. Young Francis Jehl stood by it with all the solemnity of a patriarch, and explained it lucidly to all who desired. A current passing through a galvanometer deflects a small mirror at the back of which is a tiny magnet. Opposite this mirror, at a couple of feet distance, is a board along which, horizontally laid, is a scale. Through a slit in this board a ray of light passes from a lamp. The ray falls upon the small mirror, which, as the current is stronger or weaker, casts the reflection to the right or left upon the scale opposite. As more lights are put on more electricity is needed, and Francis turns an indicator, near which is an electric light, just as they do in a gas house when more or less pressure is called for by the consumption.

" 'It may be done automatically,' said Mr. Batchelor, in answer to a gentleman's inquiry; 'but it hasn't been thought out yet.'

"The visitors seemed never tired of lighting the lamps upon the main table by simply laying one between the two long wires. Most were content to ejaculate 'Wonderful!'

"There is no particle of doubt in any one's mind that the electric light is a success and a permanent one. I spoke yesterday of the enthusiasm of a young glassblower; but it is a curious instance of Edison's brain force that this enthusiasm is common to all about the place. It is not unusual in such establishments for the inquirer to find here and there a captious understrapper who with very little encouragement will proceed to belittle their master. I have found nothing of the kind here. Edison animates the men and boys — there is scarcely a gray head in the establishment — with his own indomitable, persistent spirit. It is not merely in talking to a stranger, but in working, that this is seen.

"Edison's chief assistant, Mr. Batchelor, will glow like a carbon lamp when he is asked a question. Secretary Griffin, who sits up in the office, generates enthusiasm with eighty horsepower if you hint at a desire for information, and it is all done with bonhomie and has nothing of 'shop talk' about it. Mr. Upton is genial and answers questions with textbook exactitude, although the object or process may be only a week old. The truth is Edison attracts the right kind of people for his work, and his 'go' keeps them going. It is not mere day's work that he exacts from them or himself."

The wrinkled hand of the inventor shook slightly as he paused in reading the article. He nodded with pleasure at the way in which the reporter had written of the visitors. It was touching to recall everyone's enthusiasm and expressions of amazement over his new electric light.

"All day long and until late this evening," continued the narrative, "Menlo Park has been thronged with visitors coming from all directions to see the wonderful 'electric light.' Nearly every train that stopped brought delegations of sight-seers until the depot was overrun and the narrow plank road leading to the laboratory became alive with people. In the laboratory the throngs practically took possession of everything in their eager curiosity to learn all about the great invention. In vain Mr. Edison sought to get away and do some work, but no sooner had he struggled from one crowd than he became the center of another equally as inquisitive. The assistants likewise were plied with questions until they were obliged to suspend labor and give themselves over to answering questions. Not a little trouble was experienced in keeping the crowds from damaging the various apparatus in the laboratory. Requests and notices not to touch or handle were unavailing. One of the best of the vacuum pumps was broken by some over-meddlesome strangers, who, during the temporary absence of the attendants, began experimenting on their own account.

"Four new street lamps were last night added making six in all which now give out the horseshoe light in the open air. Their superiority to gas is so apparent, both in steadiness and beauty of illumination, that every one is struck with admiration. The laboratory office and machine shop and the houses of Mr. Batchelor and Mrs. Jordan, were all illuminated, the total number of lights being sixty. The house of Mrs. Jordan, situated near the laboratory, has been thrown open for the accommodation of guests, and having several of the electric lamps in operation affords, perhaps, the best view of the light in actual household use."

At this point in the article, the old inventor laughed aloud. He looked forward to rereading the next part of the story, as it recalled the wonderful nights of fun in the Menlo Park laboratory. What great times he and the staff had together in those bygone days. He smiled with anticipation as he continued reading the reporter's account.

"Now let me tell the story of a night with Edison. The last visitors had departed and Menlo Park was in its normal solitude. The two gray-bearded old men who had stood conversing — it seemed to me all day and all evening — at the head of the steps leading down the bank to the railroad track were gone away. Great clouds swept across the sky and the light from the hotel and grocery of Deacon Davis was the dim glare of the random kerosene lamp. All the electricity seemed to have died out of the place, and I looked about for possible occupation. Edison had gone to his house below an hour before; the boys up at the laboratory had told me that he would scarcely come back before morning, but still as I walked in the direction of the shops there was assurance of life there in the lights at the windows. Some people are at work I thought; for as I drew nearer I could see shadows flitting upon the panes. Then I heard the notes of an organ, and who would believe it in these days of progress, and above all at Menlo Park? The notes that came were those of *Pinafore*. The little outer office where they test the telephones was tenantless. In the distance a solitary, aproned figure stood before the small furnace where they bake the little carbon horseshoes, so I ascended the stairs. At the far end of the long apartment which had exchanged its electric brilliance for the light of an occasional gas jet were scattered about eight or nine of the assistants, lounging on stools and benches, and at the extreme end, seated before the organ, was one of them rolling out the too familiar melody. Then this is what came to my ears:

MacGregor —

    I am the Wizard of electric light,

Chorus —

    And a wide-awake Wizard, too.

MacGregor —

    I see you're rather bright and appreciate the might
       Of what I daily do
    Quadruplex telegraph or funny phonograph,
       It's all the same to me;
    With ideas I evolve and problems that I solve
       I am never, never stumped, you see . . .

"A groan escaped from my bosom, and the line was left un-completed. It is evident, I thought, that Edison is not coming back tonight. They called out to me, and I came forward shocked, positively shocked. And there was no trace of apology for this desecration of the fame of science in the tones of Mr. Batchelor when he said: 'We're having a little music. Sit down and join us.'

"MacGregor at the organ was still rolling off *Pinafore*, then 'switching off' into Strauss and 'letting her have a full current' of Offenbach.

"We're going to have a grand piano here for the boys shortly. That organ's frightfully out of tune.'

"So it was, and the sturdy Mac was like the organ, but the boys listened to him as intently as Joseffy's audiences. Van Cleff came down the shop holding a black piece of iron in a tongs. He laid it on a bench to cool, for it was not long out of the furnace. Then he took one like it and began unscrewing it to place the cardboard horseshoes in it that were to be carbonized. Boehm, the glassblower, came up in his best attire.

" 'Say, Boehm, bring up your zither,' said George Crosby, who all day long had been working the delicate vacuum pumps and now rested for a space.

" 'Up here?' said Boehm, blushing; 'play here, now?' looking over doubtfully at me.

" 'Go ahead!' said Batchelor; 'that organ's in a terrible state.'

"Boehm brought up the zither from the glass house and laid it on the bench before him. Crosby forced MacGregor away from the organ. The German lad sat down and tuned the strings.

Thomas Edison as he appeared in 1879

" 'I had a good teacher at Bonn,' he said, slowly, 'but I forget much.'

"He began to play, and all the grimy faces bent forward to listen. It was a quaint German serenade, that sounded as though far away from the focal point of materialism we occupied. There was something of dreamy moonlight on the Rhine in the tinkling treble and moaning bass strings.

" 'That's lovely music,' said MacGregor.

" 'Boehm,' said Batchelor, 'play something else with those shake notes in it; they go right down my back.'

" 'Shake notes? What is that?'

" 'Tremolo,' I suggested. He played again an exquisite melody, and Batchelor bent forward, as he put it in his material way, that would reduce every emotion to the stimulation of a particular ganglion, so he might feel the music going 'right down his back.'

"But during the playing a man with a crumpled felt hat, a white silk handkerchief at his throat, his coat hanging carelessly and his vest half buttoned, came silently in, and, with his hand to his ear, sat close by the glassblower, who, wrapped up in his music, was back perhaps in his native Thuringia again.

" 'That's nice,' said he, looking round. It was Edison.

"The glassblower played on, and the scene was curious. Standing by a blazing gas furnace he had lighted, Van Cleff with bare folded arms, listened or else shifted the hot irons with his pincers, but he did it gently. Edison sat bent forward. The others who had taken up one tool or another moved them slowly. Far back through the half-darkened shop young Jehl might be seen lifting the heavy bottles of gleaming quicksilver at the vacuum pumps, and the soft music was delicately thrilling through it all. It was the wedding of spirit and matter, and impressed me strangely.

" 'Can you play "The Heart Bowed Down?" ' said Edison, suddenly.

" 'No, I cannot.'

" 'Here, whistle it, some of you.' Five or six whistled, and Boehm shook his head.

" 'Can't play it? Well, Crosby, what's that other tune?'

" 'My poor heart is sad with its dreaming,' said Crosby.

" 'Yes, play that?'

" 'I cannot.'

" 'Play anything,' said Crosby, 'it's all the same to him and us.'
Boehm played. Edison seemed to be fidgeting about 'The Heart
Bowed Down.' He took a writing pad from his pocket and
scratched rapidly with a pencil on it for some minutes. He beckon-
ed to Boehm.

" 'Can you blow that?' He handed him a rough drawing.

" 'Yes,' said the boy, 'you mean that for a circle? Yes; that
will be better.'

"In a minute, zither and glassblower were gone, and they took
all the dreamy spirit of fatherland with them. The concert was
over. It was about half past ten. Conversation turned on scientific
topics, roaming over wide fields, the boyish assistants breaking in
here and there like young colts, Batchelor turning round now
and again from his minute study of finished carbons to declaim
with more than ordinary emphasis on particular points. Owing to
Edison's slight defect of hearing we naturally spoke rather loud,
and that conversation would have sounded oddly in any stranger's
ears. The acuteness of Edison's perceptions was what struck me
most, and often desultory as our talk seemed, he struck off keen
observations that surprised me. I felt rather in doubt whether I
ought to go down to my sleeping place or remain, and about elev-
en o'clock I asked Edison if he was going to work or going home.

" 'That's just as it strikes him,' said one near me in an ordinary
voice.

" 'Are you in a hurry?' said Edison. 'I'm not.'

"I'd like to see some of your platinum lamps,' I said, 'if it's not
troublesome.'

" 'Come over here,' and he led the way to a glass case in the
corner, where a medley of contorted glass globes and tubing lay
upon cotton wool. He took some of them out and explained
them — how low the resistance of platinum was compared with
carbon, and so on; how he coated the fine wire with almost
infusible oxides to insulate it, so that in nine feet of it reeled

around a bobbin the electric fluid would have to run along the entire length of it.

" 'I ransacked the world,' said he, 'for scarce metals and spent lots of money in reducing ores. I have little bottles here that cost me a couple of hundred dollars.'

" 'Didn't you find the text books and authorities save you a great deal of time in these matters?'

" 'They're mostly misleading," said he sturdily. 'I get mad with myself when I think I have believed what was so learnedly set out in them.'

" ' What,' I said, aghast, 'are the books wrong?'

" 'I'll tell you what I mean; there are more frauds in science than anywhere else. There are two classes of them — first, the pure scientists without practical knowledge, and next the practical men without any science. You take the pure scientist —mind you, I don't speak of such men as Faraday, Regnault or Bunsen, nor such men as Maxwell, or Sir William Thompson; what they say is so is so, because they proved it before they said so; but take a whole pile of them that I can name and you will find uncertainty if not imposition in half of what they state as scientific truth. These men did not work for money, and they had only reputation to work for. They have time and again set down experiments as done by them, curious out-of-the-way experiments that they never did and upon which they founded so-called scientific truths. I have been thrown off the track often by them, and for months at a time. You see a great name and you believe in it. Try the experiment yourself and you find the result altogether different.'

" 'Can you name some of these so-called truths?'

" 'Yes, plenty. I tell you, to an earnest inquirer books are a detriment. Say, Van Cleff,' said the bold young man raising his voice, 'bring me the *Dictionary of Solubilities*.'

"It was brought up from some recesses downstairs.

" 'Look here,' he continued; 'with common things that nobody wants to test they'll serve you well enough. Ah! here,' he pointed to an oxide of baryta; 'Look: one says, "insoluble in water," another, "sparingly soluble in water." So it goes. You will find here sometimes fifty authorities, all giving different statements about one thing. Do you see that name, there, given as an authority? That man wrote a book on the art of scientific discovery, and he never made but two or three little bits of discovery in his life. Now, you'd think platinum was pretty well known, but the books say it is infusible except in an oxyhydrogen flame. Why,' and he laughed, 'I can melt it in the flame of a candle. Come here; I'll melt some in that gas jet.'

"We crossed the laboratory and he took up a spool of very fine platinum wire, broke off about nine inches of it and held it in the gas jet. It shriveled up, but held together. I looked at him incredulously.

" 'Hey, Francis, bring me that microscope.'

"Frances in due time appeared with a large instrument, green with verdigris. Edison laughed as I looked at it.

" 'Oh,' said he, 'we keep things here for use. That cost $300, but I've had ten times its value out of it. Haeckel, Evolutionist Haeckel, you know, never uttered a truer thing than when talking about laboratories with costly instruments kept shut up in glass cases, he said the quantity of work done was in inverse proportion to the quantity of apparatus.' Adjusting the microscope, he continued, 'Look in here now. You see along the magnified wire a number of little globules, that is where the platinum has fused, and I can do it in a candle. They talk without much thinking. They found a thick wire wouldn't melt in a gas flame, so they said platinum couldn't be melted there. If they were the first to discover water they'd say you couldn't boil it, because they tried burning a tallow candle under a cask of it.'

" 'Are you an evolutionist?'

" 'Oh, yes: I believe in that. This is magnesium; of course you've seen it burn,' and he tore off a piece of the ribbon and lighted it. It flamed out. 'The peculiar moonlight color in the voltaic arc light is due to the impurities in the carbon, magnesium among the rest. What's the matter with you, Francis?'

he said, turning to young Jehl, who was sitting moodily by.

" 'I'm hungry,' blurted out Francis.

" 'Where's the lunch?' said Edison.

" 'There was none ordered,' said Francis, more despondently; 'we didn't think you were coming back to work all night, and now we're here and there's nothing.'

" 'Get us something to eat,' said Edison. 'You see, the carbon used is made out of powder, held together by various substances. If they were to use chemically pure carbon, they would place the light away out of reach, it would cost so much; and pure or not, they must use a foreign substance to make it hold together. George, bring me a stick of carbon and a filament.'

"He put the little filament under the microscope and it looked like a cake of coal. Then he broke off a piece of the carbon stick and heated it with a blowpipe to show the impurities under the microscope.

" 'You said a while ago that books and authorities were a detriment; that seems very strong to me.'

" 'Remember how I qualified it. But I tell you I'd rather know nothing about a thing in science nine times out of ten than what the books could tell me — for practical purposes, for applied science, the best science, the only science. I'd rather take the thing up and go through with it myself. I'd find out more about it than any one could tell me, and I'd be sure of what I knew. That's the thing. Professor-this or -that will controvert you out of the books, and prove out of the books that it can't be so, though you have it right in the hollow of your hand all the time and could break his spectacles with it. I never take anybody's word that anything can't be done, if I as much as suspect it can. I showed you in that book over there how they trip each other up.

" 'We had to make phosphoric anhydride for the vacuum pumps, and that's a job. We light the phosphorus and run. The vapor of it is terrible, but it's nothing to osmic acid. You remember a great Parisian scientist once held up a vial of it and said there was enough to suffocate the entire population of

Paris if they were passed through in a file. I thought that was too strong. I took just a little sniff of it once, and I tell you it was terrible — the worst I ever came near. It stung my nose and caught me in the throat.

" 'The book was right that time. That was the right kind of scientist.'

"It was well after midnight now, and I heard some of the boys tramping upstairs, while Edison now with the peculiar nocturnal brightening of the human owl, talked in an unbroken string about the strange metals with unfamiliar names he had such apparent fun in reducing.

" 'I think the Almighty made carbon especially for the electric light. What's this for?' George held something in a brown paper out before him.

" 'Herrings,' said George; 'smoked herrings.'

"Edison looked around glumly. 'Is this the best you can do?' Francis was seated on a stool, a herring in one hand, a cracker in the other, his mouth full of cracker and herring and his whole face beaming.

" 'He's happy,' said Edison, 'Help yourself; we don't entertain in this way.'

" 'Pot luck,' said the *Herald* correspondent, cheerfully.

" 'Everything agrees with me,' said Edison. So the repast went on. We were a merry crowd of seven there at one in the morning. The inventor's face beamed with good humor, and he joked with the boys who are on such a pleasant footing with him, intimate in expression, but it was always a pleasure to see the respectful alacrity with which they looked after him at all times; just now they were looking for tender herrings for him. Francis, from smiles and laughing gradually assumed a more settled expression indicating that the process of digestion was rapidly taking place, and in a very short time he was asleep on the edge of one of the benches, with the *Dictionary of Solubilities* for a pillow. One by one they dropped off. George actually went to have a look at his vacuum pump before curling up on a bench, and Edison and the *Herald* man, with just one other who, however, took three sleeps meantime sat talking till four o'clock. What did he talk of? Well, who could tell. Like a fresh-hearted city boy out in the fields for a holiday, he ran through the gardens of science in a way at once fascinating and surprising. Reminiscences of old times when he was a telegraph operator jogged elbows with dissertations on chemistry, electricity, light, heat, dynamics, statics.

"As I was leaving the laboratory I saw the inventor with his coat over his arm, looking for a soft spot upon the benches."

Thus, with Edison in search of a place to sleep, the stirring and graphic account ended. The remarkable demonstration at Menlo Park was over, but the memory of its magic would live forever. To the old man, sitting alone now in his West Orange laboratory, it had marked the beginning of a busy and hurried career. Recalling those long ago and trying times, the elderly Edison got up slowly from his chair. He returned the worn newspaper to its resting place in the drawer, then stood for a moment looking out of the laboratory window.

From across the way, in one of the huge brick buildings, he could see the efficient movements of his many employees. Their hustling reminded him once more of that faded day in 1880 when his Menlo Park staff had brought order to the laboratory once more. The crowds had left the place disorganized and it took several hours to get things straight. The old man smiled to himself as he thought of the men stirring about like housewives in an attempt to clean up the place. Batchelor had stood in the midst of the confusion, shaking a sorrowful head.

"Mr. Edison," he moaned, "it will take forever to get everything back in shape."

The young inventor laughed. "Well, Batch, do the best you can. After all, the world doesn't see something like the light every day."

The weary assistant nodded, but with little enthusiasm. It had been a hectic several days and he longed to get back to normal work. With sagging shoulders, he left the inventor to his own thoughts and sauntered off with a hopeless air. Edison

The Menlo Park staff on the second floor of the laboratory after the invention of the electric light

surveyed the scene about him. Tables were askew, bulbs had been either broken or stolen, and the floor bore the marks of several thousand shoes. He chuckled to himself.

The search for the first successful electric light was over, but the total creation of a new industry lay ahead. In his mind, he had already conceived of the hundreds of new inventions required to successfully light a city: switches, fuses, meters, underground cables, powerful dynamos, millions of lamps, gigantic generators and engineering principles as yet unheard-of.

He looked about him for a moment, noting that the men were oblivious to everything except their work. It pleased him to know that his staff was forever loyal and would follow him in any endeavor. Their conduct during the New Year's exhibit had been admirable and he intended to thank them fully. Right now, however, it was best to not disturb them as their hours had been long and strenuous.

The young inventor thought of his next project while the men swept and cleaned. So far, it was outlined only in his head and he had said nothing about it. If Batchelor and the others knew his plans, they might indeed shake in their boots. There was always time tomorrow to inform them; and besides, it was late now and the men needed their rest.

With that, he scratched his head slowly, then descended the laboratory stairs, whistling as he went.

He was headed for the library and a chance to think about his next job.

Thomas Edison was going to light New York City.

Thomas Edison about the time he lighted New York City

Genius And Generators

TO SOME OLD MEN, the past becomes confused with the present. But this was never the case with Thomas Edison. Even though he was now past eighty, his mental capacity still remained strong and his memories were exceedingly clear. Settled in his giant West Orange laboratory — a veritable monument to his genius — the elderly inventor still held the esteem of fellow industrialists. His black-clad figure was known around the world and newspaper reporters always looked upon him as "good copy."

Today, as he conducted further experiments in his laboratory, the old man could not help but think of his past. As he mixed powdered chemicals with a stirring rod, his mind reviewed the bygone days at Menlo Park. The electric light was then a reality, but the origination of a lighting system was yet to come. The year 1880 had rolled around and Edison, still a young and energetic man, agreed with several aldermen from New York to light a district of that great city.

The aldermen had visited Menlo Park during the New Year's demonstration. Their interest and enthusiasm in Edison's miraculous invention was intense. After viewing the brilliantly lighted community, they immediately asked the inventor to consider the illumination of New York. At first, he felt some doubt about tackling such a project, as he did not know what would be involved; but before the year had passed away, he decided to give it a try, realizing that hundreds of items would have to be invented.

As an old man, absorbed with experimentation at West

Orange, he recalled his feeling at that time about such a project.

"There was nothing we could buy," he thought to himself, "or that anyone could make for us."

Knowing this, he finally agreed to tackle the project of lighting a section of New York. After the New Year's exhibit chaos was over, he called his staff together and informed them of his decision. They were not the least bit perturbed, as he suspected they might be, and right away offered their help. Encouraged by his employees' loyalty, Edison set to work and quickly organized the Edison Illuminating Company; with such a charter organization established, he then plunged into the job at hand — namely, the creation of every possible electrical apparatus needed to light a city.

One of the first projects on the busy agenda was, of course, the manufacture of lamp bulbs at Menlo Park. As the task became more involved, Edison organized a separate lamp company at Harrison, New Jersey, and production got under way immediately. One of the problems facing the inventor was the cost of the shiny glass bulbs; in order to sell, they must be available at a modest price, but in the beginning he found that the bulbs cost at least $1.25 apiece.

As a revered and aged inventor, the old man recalled this problem of cost with a shake of his head. The black brows knitted closely together as he spoke of his dilemma.

"The fourth year," he would shout, "I got the cost down to 37c and with a 3c profit per lamp, made up in one year all the money I'd lost previously. I finally got it down to 22c, sold them for 40c, and they were made by the millions."

But in the beginning, in 1880, his problem was to get at least four hundred globes ready for the lighting of the New York district. This task was undertaken with all speed and before long, the lamps were rolling off the production line.

Meanwhile, back at Menlo Park, there were a million things to do. One of the most gigantic problems was the design of a powerful generator. It would require a tremendous amount of electricity to light the proposed district and Edison's problem was to supply it. He went immediately to the Porter Steam Engine Company and quickly told them of his requirements. In later years, as the patriarch of American inventors, he related this important and unusual visit.

"There were no high-speed engines in these days," he recalled. "I decided that the magneto should be taken up where Faraday had started it. There was no way to build a great electrical industry until the machinery was developed. I conceived the idea of a direct-coupled machine, and wanted to hitch the dynamo direct to the engine without belting. The engine builders held up their hands and said, 'Impossible!' I called C. H. Porter and said to him: 'Mr. Porter, I want a 150-horse-power engine to run 700 revolutions a minute.' He hummed and hawed a bit and then agreed to build it. We set the machine up in the old shop, and I had some idea of what might happen. So we tied a chain round the throttle and ran it out through a window into the woodshed, where we stood to work it. The shop stood on one of those New Jersey shale hills, and every time we opened up the engine and she got to about 300 revolutions, the whole hill shook under her. We shut her off and rebalanced, and tried again, and, after a good deal of trouble, we finally did run up to 700, but you should have seen her run! Why, every time the connecting rod went up, she tried to lift that whole hill with her! After we got through with this business we tamed her down to 350 revolutions (which was all I wanted). We closed a bill with Porter for six engines.

"While all this was going on in the shop, we had dug ditches and laid mains all around the district (through which to supply power). I used to sleep nights on piles of pipes in the station, and I saw every box poured and every connection made on the whole job. I had to! There was nobody else who could superintend it. Finally we got our feeders all down and started to put on an engine and turn one of the machines to see how things were. My heart was in my mouth at first, but everything worked all right and we had more than 500 ohms insulation resistance. Then we started another engine and threw them in parallel.

"Of all the circuses since Adam was born, we had the worst then. One engine would stop, and the other would run up to about a thousand revolutions and then they would seesaw.

"What was the matter? Why, it was these Porter governors! When the circus commenced, the men who were standing round ran out precipitately, and some of them kept running for a block or two. I grabbed the throttle of one engine, and E. H. Johnson, who was the only one present who kept his wits, caught hold of the other and we shut them off. Of course I discovered then that what had happened was that one set was running the other one as a motor.

"I then put up a long shaft connecting all the governors together, and thought this would certainly cure the trouble, but it didn't. The torsion of the shaft was so great that one governor managed still to get ahead of the others. Then I got a piece of shafting and a tube in which it fitted. I twisted the shaft one way and the tube the other, as far as I could, and pinned them together. In this way, by straining the whole outfit up to its elastic limit in opposite directions, the torsion was practically eliminated, and after that the governors ran together all right.

"Somewhere about that time I got hold of Gardiner C. Sims, and he undertook to build an engine to run at 350 revolutions and give 175 horse power. He went back to Providence and set to work and brought the engine back with him. It worked, but only for a few minutes, when it busted. That man sat around that shop and slept in it for three weeks until he got his engine right and made it work the way he wanted it to.

"When he reached this period, I gave orders for the works to run night and day until we got enough engines, and when all was ready, we started the main engine. The date was September 4, 1882, a Saturday night. That was when we first turned the current on to the mains for regular light distribution, and it stayed on for eight years with only one insignificant stoppage. One of these engines that Sims built ran twenty-four hours a day for 365 days before it was stopped to give it a rest."

Over the next few days, Edison worked feverishly in preparation for the lighting of the New York district. He took out over three hundred patents covering his new inventions and in 1881, had opened a New York office at No. 65 Fifth Avenue. His time was spent in countless trips between Menlo Park and the great city — consulting, checking, probing, testing and satisfying himself that the work was progressing as specified.

After many trying hours, he finally designed an efficient dynamo, dubbed the "Long-Waisted Mary Ann," and set up a shop for the manufacture of the units. In later years, he vividly recalled the establishments of his many production plants and spoke of them with a smile.

"I took over the old Etna Iron Works on Goerck Street, surrounded by tumbled-down old tenement houses, on the East side of New York," he said. "We ran this as the Edison Machine Works, my first factory for dynamos, but the business grew so fast that we finally removed to Schenectady. We began to manufacture our meters, chandeliers, sockets, and switches in the little shop of Sigmund Bergmann, in Wooster Street. Bergmann had worked at the bench for me in Newark and then started the Wooster Street shop, where he built some of my phonographs. This is the Bergmann who finally became owner of the great electrical industries in Berlin.

"Our shops were all so busy that John Kruesi was brought over from Menlo Park to Harrison, New Jersey, and we had our hands full."

One day, in the early stages of the preliminary planning, Edison toyed with the idea of an electrical railway. It seemed to him that one of the new dynamos could be laid out horizontally and equipped with wheels so that the electrical power would turn them. He studied the idea and finally, after much designing, came up with a satisfactory locomotive. This was a crude affair, boasting a cab and cow-catcher on the front; several wooden cars were built which, when pulled by the locomotive, traveled at a speed of forty miles per hour. Tracks were then laid near the Menlo Park laboratory and the little train was put into operation.

On several occasions, the locomotive jumped the track, tumbl-

Edison in the cab of his electric railway at Menlo Park

ing its passengers upon the ground. Edison always laughed till he shook and would help the startled victims to their shaky feet. This sort of fun offered some diversion from the New York lighting project, but, although several financial wizards expressed an interest in it, the electric train brought nothing into the Edison bank account.

"As usual," Edison laughed, "I paid for the experiment."

Time flew by in preparing for the tremendous lighting project. Edison acquired a multistoried building in New York in which to house the world's first power station. The structure, solid and practical for his purposes, was located at 257 Pearl Street. All manner of machinery and equipment was moved into the building and the workmen labored relentlessly to get things promptly in order.

The district chosen for the project was one in lower Manhattan. Before long, it was dubbed the "First District" by everyone connected with the tremendous task. Edison still worked alongside his men with shirtsleeves rolled up and a determined look upon his brow; he continued digging trenches in the streets for underground cables and hardly took time to eat or sleep. When the first dynamos were installed in the station, he supervised every connection and stood by to see that the men had no difficulty. The dynamos were veritable giants, coupled to a tremendous 150 horsepower steam engine. They weighed twenty-seven tons apiece and where most machines ran at sixty revolutions per minute, the Edison dynamos were capable of a seven hundred rpm operation. This was unheard-of in the industrial world and represented but one of the many revolutionary inventions created by the young inventor.

At last, as time flew by, and September of 1882 arrived, the station was ready for operation. The First District had been completely wired and equipped. Edison meanwhile had acquired many new customers for his lighting company and their premises now boasted new fixtures and equipment; among the list of businesses in the district were the banking firm of Drexel, Morgan and Company . . . the newspaper offices of the "Herald" and "Times" . . .

The "Long-Waisted Mary Ann" dynamo invented by Edison

and Sweet's Restaurant on Fulton Street. The total number of lamps installed amounted to four hundred, a splendid beginning for the first project. All of New York read of the proposed experiment and looked forward to its completion.

Finally, the evening of September 4th arrived and, with it, the first demonstration of electric lighting in the First District. Edison, his eyes alert and his hand steady, threw the master switch which controlled the plant operation. All at once, the generators and dynamos whirred with unexcelled power and the entire station echoed their rumblings. The young inventor stepped near a large window, looking down upon the darkened streets and buildings below; he carefully placed his hand upon a precision control and with one deliberate movement, threw the switch.

Of a sudden, the streets of the First District became alive with light. The brilliance of four hundred lamps shone through the once darkened night. Through the windows of countless buildings, the dazzling light shone out like many beacons. The shouts and cries of the crowds assembled for the demonstration rose in a frenzy. Thomas Edison had succeeded — he had brought the miracle of light to New York City.

The young inventor, surrounded by the admiring public, smiled modestly as he beheld the sight before him. His labors had not been in vain and the fame of this achievement would be spread by telegraph throughout the country. The one-time "addled" schoolboy had won over seemingly insurmountable obstacles and now stood looking down on the reward for his labors. At the height of this night's success, he thought how proud his wife, Mary, would be of his work; without her encouragement and understanding he might not have been able to accomplish this miracle.

The crowds surged through the lighted streets, tossing hats and yells of victory into the air. They pushed against the Pearl Street station, hoping to see the young genius who had so blessed their city.

"Hurrah for Edison," they screamed. "Let's see Edison . . . Bring him out!"

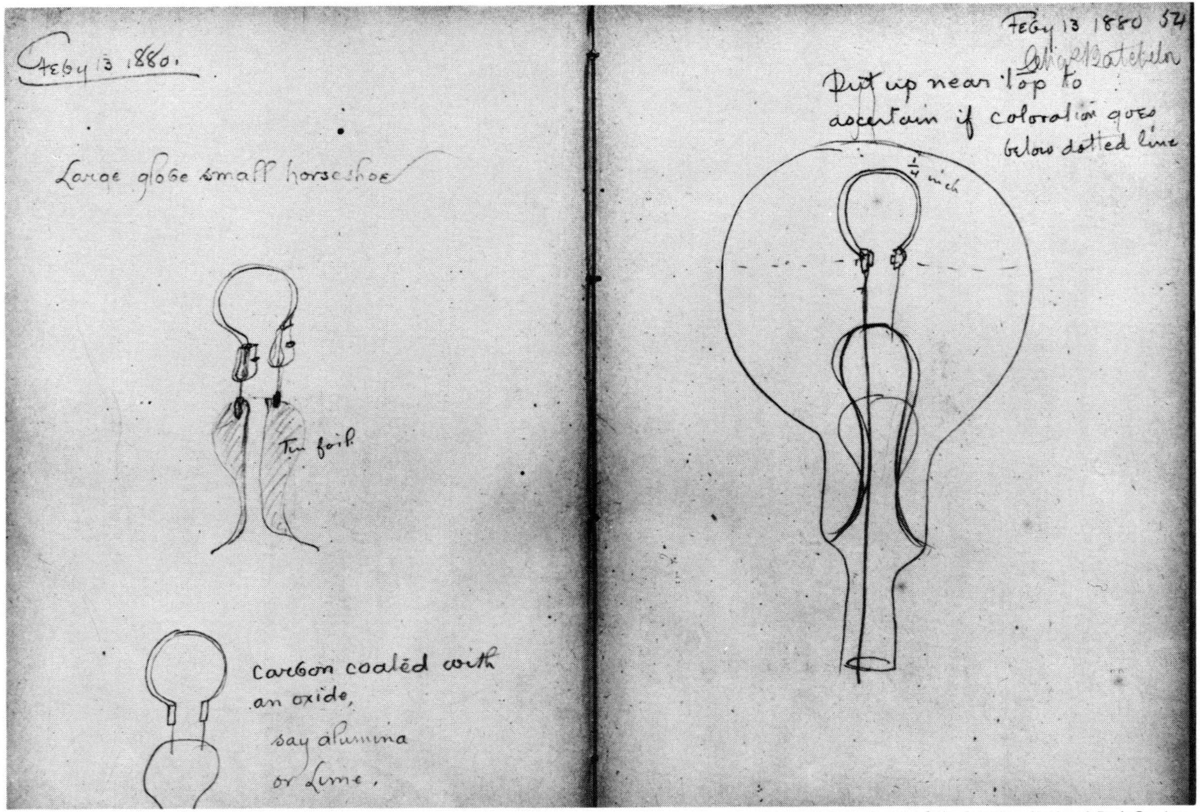
Feby 13 1880.
Large globe small horseshoe
Tin foil
Carbon coated with
an oxide,
say alumina
or Lime,
Feby 13 1880 54
Put up near top to
ascertain if coloration goes
below dotted line
1/4 inch

Courtesy Department of the Interior, National Park Service

Pages from Edison's laboratory notebook, illustrating the "Edison Effect" bulb

It was a gala evening, never to be forgotten in New York City. In Sweet's Restaurant, the crystal chandeliers glowed with beautiful light as elegantly dressed diners enjoyed a delicious repast. At the bank building, the soft light bathed the solid-paneled offices in beauty, as the officials happily guided the many visitors on an eye-filling tour. The aldermen, who originally had approached Edison on lighting lower Manhattan, beamed with pleasure at the magnificent accomplishment of the inventor. Everyone that memorable night — with the exception of the gas industry — was elated and filled with admiration for Thomas Edison.

The most proud would indeed be the inventor's wife. For all of these years at Menlo Park, she had stood faithfully by her husband. Mary Edison was a modest woman, working diligently at keeping their home and raising the children, Marion, Thomas Junior and William. She never complained about her husband's irregular hours and always understood his every mood, whether enthusiastic or dejected.

Her pride in Edison was unbounded. She recognized him as a genius who required love and deep understanding. He never failed to receive her undivided attention on matters he wished to discuss with her. She was always there, ready to hear him out and place an encouraging hand upon his shoulder. Now, with the lighting of New York City, Mary's pride went soaring as she remembered tenderly — yet with a touch of sadness — the months of toil it had cost her husband.

For many months now, while Edison had labored at his work, she had suffered from a form of neuralgia. The pain would shoot through her body, leaving her almost exhausted; yet not once did she complain to her young husband, lest it disturb him and take him away from his work. Mary loved him with all her tender heart, never wanting to upset his busy routine.

Edison thought of her with warmth and love as he stood in the Pearl Street station. She is blessed among women, he felt, and he hoped that she was indeed proud of him.

The rest of that night reflected Edison's glory in this wonderful demonstration. The electric lamps continued to glow through the darkness and the crowds continued in pandemonium.

The Wizard of Menlo Park was truly the hero of the hour.

The months following that glorious night brought more funds into the coffers of the enterprise. By the end of that year, Edison's company boasted two hundred and forty customers who were served by more than five thousand lamps. Meanwhile, research continued in order to improve operations and Edison continued to file patents covering his discoveries. While experimenting one day, he found that a plate, set between the legs of a filament in a lamp, would react like a valve to control the flow of current; the inventor was not certain what use this discovery might be, but he dubbed it the "Edison Effect" and filed a patent on it. At the time, he did not know that his creation, in the hands of others, would be the basis for the foundation of modern electronics.

His success was heralded around the world. Every newspaper in foreign countries carried the amazing story of his work in the electrical field. The young inventor was riding the crest of fame. There was very little in the way of honor that had not come his way. As he traveled between New York and Menlo Park, he often read flattering accounts of his work and plans.

Then the tragedy struck.

It was August 9, 1884. Edison had been working steadily in New York and at the old laboratory in Menlo Park. He knew that his wife, Mary, had not felt well the past few days. His concern for her had mounted until he almost felt it dangerous to leave her side. Today, because of tremendous tasks confronting him, he had walked to the laboratory to work for a while. He sat deeply engrossed in the problem at hand, but the thought of Mary nagged at him.

Finally, tossing his work aside, he went home. Mary was tucked in her bed, smiling as usual when her illustrious husband entered the room. The expression on her face reflected deep pain and Edison, for the first time in his life, felt helpless. He rushed to his wife, taking hold of the soft and gentle hand. She gazed deeply into his eyes and whispered that she loved him. His heart pounded with anxiety over Mary's painful condition. He talked to her for a long time, comforting the wrinkled brow and attempting to cheer her up.

Before he realized what had happened, Mary Stilwell Edison smiled at him for the last time. Her beautiful and radiant face turned to a mask of stillness as death came to her. Edison's head fell in remorse and sobs welled up inside of him.

Mary was gone.

His frame shook with grief as night fell slowly upon them. Only the soft glow of his electric lamp remained to illumine the delicate features of his dead wife.

It was over . . . and Thomas Edison, the world renowned genius, was alone.

Labor And Love

THE WEATHERED OLD DEAN of invention sat in his library at the West Orange laboratory. His wrinkled hand was making notes of things he wanted to remember. The desk at which he sat was a huge roll-top affair, crammed with papers and scraps of reminders. His yellow stub pencil glided slowly across a ruled note pad as the old man jotted down a message to himself. Sometime, he thought silently, he might want to use these words, so it was best to record them now.

"My desire," he wrote slowly, "is to do everything within my power to free the people from drudgery, and create the largest measure of happiness and prosperity."

He laid his pencil down, carefully reading his words. His eyes fell upon one in particular — "happiness." There had been a time when he felt happiness had vanished from his life forever. With a touch of long-healed sadness, he now thought of Mary and the effect of her death upon him. What grief to have lost her — what uncontrolled bitterness had come into his life way back there. His old hand shook as he folded the tablet sheet and placed it in an already crowded slot of the desk.

The old man got up and shuffled to the library door. It was time to get back to his experiment at the workbench. Busy hands prevented old wounds from springing to life and helped forget past grievances. He quietly left the enormous room and headed deliberately down the hall toward the laboratory. It was much like the time, way back in 1884, when he plunged into work after Mary had died.

In those days, he came to almost despise Menlo Park and

spent more and more of his time in New York. With three young children in his charge, the inventor found it difficult to take care of them. He finally turned to Mary's mother, a most kind and understanding woman, who lived in New York; she took the children under her loving care, allowing their father to continue his work without excessive worry.

Menlo Park gradually was turned over to the ghosts of the past. Edison removed his mass of equipment from the old buildings and quietly shipped it to New York. Afterward, the laboratory fell into misuse and over the years to come, fell into a state of deterioration. The saga of Menlo Park, as far as the inventor was concerned, had passed. There were too many memories in the little hamlet, so Edison deserted it and decided never to return again.

Meanwhile in New York, he continued his management of the electric company. Business was excellent and his research in this new industry was tireless. The faithful old staff — including Jehl, Batchelor and Upton — continued to work by his side and were given responsible assignments. Now that Mary was gone, these wonderful co-workers and friends seemed to fill an empty void.

During this period, the great mind of Edison conceived many new inventions. He labored at the problem of wireless telegraphy for a while, coming up with a system of the wireless for communication between railway stations and moving trains. On March 27, 1885, he filed a patent on the invention and turned to other areas in the telegraphic field.

His next venture was to establish a successful means of ship-to-shore wireless, by means of induction. Once satisfied with the improvement, he again sent his patent papers to Washington. For much of his life, a love for telegraphy crept into his activities and remained of interest until the close of his career.

On occasion, to break the monotony of routine, the inventor would take a brief holiday from his work. By now, he claimed many personal friends and often visited in their homes. One such friend was Ezra T. Gilliland, who had assisted Edison in his work

Thomas Edison as he appeared three years prior
to his marriage to Mina Miller

on the wireless telegraph. Both he and his kind wife took an interest in the inventor and hoped that some day he might remarry. In 1885, they invited their friend, Edison, to their home in Boston for a few days; he accepted promptly and, upon his arrival, found the Gillilands had become involved in "matchmaking." A bevy of young ladies flitted in and out of their house, smiling daintily at the renowned inventor. He promptly ignored them.

As their house guest, Edison was next entertained with an evening at the theater. He remarked that he sat in "bald-head row" and that the show had, as expected, "the usual number of servant girls in tights." Then, of a sudden, the stage lights brightened to usher on the star of the evening, the glamorous Lillian Russell. This statuesque female sang gloriously and inspired Edison to whisper in Gilliland's ear.

"Beautiful woman," he remarked, "beautiful voice."

The next day, according to a carefully laid plan of Mrs. Gilliland's, a striking young woman appeared at their home. Her name was Mina Miller and she had come from Akron, Ohio. It seemed that she and the plotting Mr. Gilliland had been close friends for a period of time. The girl's father, Lewis Miller, was a wealthy industrialist in Akron, manufacturing a popular line of farm tools. The young graceful daughter immediately captured the heart of Thomas Edison. He felt that most women were flowery when introduced to him, but this girl looked him straight in the eye. There was no fake flattery about her.

That day, meeting Edison for the first time, Mina Miller became attracted to him also. Later, she sat at the piano and sang several melodic songs. The inventor became completely absorbed not only with her talent, but with the beautiful face and attractive figure. He was twice her age, but the palpitating of his heart told him it did not matter. She was the most gorgeous creature he had ever seen.

From this time on, Edison and Mina Miller saw a great deal of one another. He immediately taught her the telegraph code, so that they could tap out messages on one another's palms. Their fingers rapidly entwined and secretly, through the code, they could talk to one another. In later years, the old inventor commented on this sly system.

"My later courtship," he said, "was carried on by telegraph. I taught the lady of my heart the Morse code, and when she could both send and receive we got along much better than we could have with spoken words, by tapping our remarks to one another on our hands."

When Edison finally returned to New York, he could not rid his mind of Miss Mina. She was constantly in his memory and the thought of her terribly interfered with his sleep. Edison, in a letter written about this time, expressed his preoccupation with the young woman.

"Saw a lady who looked like Mina," he wrote. "Got thinking about Mina and came near being run over by a streetcar. If Mina interferes much more will have to take out an accident policy."

Later that winter, Edison was called to Chicago on company business. It was bitter cold and the raw wind was like ice. Due to exposure to such weather, he came down with an illness and was promptly confined to bed. The setback left him weak and in need of sunshine. When he was able to get up and about, the inventor eagerly headed for Florida in dire need of rest. He became fascinated with the tropical lushness of the place and decided, after some deliberation, to purchase a thirteen-acre tract of land near Fort Myers. It was here, near a romantic river, that he planned to build a winter home and hoped some day to bring the charming Mina here as his wife.

Not long after his return, Edison asked the lovely girl if she would go with him on an excursion through the New Hampshire mountains. The Gillilands were going, of course, to act as chaperones. Mina laughingly agreed and in no time, they found themselves in a carriage driving up the winding roads of New Hampshire. Edison snuggled close to the wonderful Mina and took her hand in his. Quietly and carefully, the inventor's fingers tapped upon her palm. It was their special code and the message caused her heart to flutter. Edison, long years afterward, told of the experience in his own words.

"I asked her thus in Morse code if she would marry me. The word 'yes' is an easy one to send by telegraphic signals, and she sent it. If she had been obliged to speak she might have found it much harder. Nobody knew anything about our many long conversations . . . If we had spoken words others would have heard them. We could use pet names without the least embarrassment."

So it was that the couple became happily engaged. Edison proceeded with his plans in Fort Myers and even talked the Gillilands into moving there. He then sent two agents down to Florida to take care of his business; in addition to a dwelling there, the inventor also wished to build another laboratory so that he might experiment while visiting. Edison promptly sat down and wrote a note of instruction for the agents. His hand raced across the paper as he set the ideas down.

"We will erect two dwellings (the Gillilands were to inhabit one of them) on the riverfront and place the laboratory and dwellings for the workmen on the other side of the street . . . Our buildings are being made in Maine and will be loaded aboard ship at Boston. We will send four of our employees to superintend the work."

In the meanwhile — and because he was a man of strict procedure — the inventor felt he should write Mina's father, asking for permission to marry her. He sat down and carefully addressed a letter to the Ohio manufacturer. In a bold copper script, the eager Edison wrote of his intentions. It was an earnest plea and was addressed from New York on September 30, 1885. It read simply, but with much feeling:

"My Dear Sir

"Some months since, as you are aware, I was introduced to your daughter Miss Mina. The friendship which ensued became admiration as I began to appreciate her gentleness and grace of manner, and her beauty and strength of mind.

"That admiration has on my part ripened into love, and I have asked her to become my wife. She has re-

ferred me to you, and our engagement needs but for its confirmation your consent.

"I trust you will not accuse me of egotism when I say that my life and history and standing are so well known as to call for no statement concerning myself. My reputation is so far made that I recognize I must be judged by it for good or ill.

"I need only add in conclusion that the step I have taken in asking your daughter to intrust her happiness into my keeping has been the result of mature deliberation, and with the full appreciation of the responsibility I have assumed, and the duty I have undertaken to fulfill.

"I do not deny that your answer will seriously affect my happiness, and I trust my suit may meet with your approval.

"Very sincerely yours

"Thomas A. Edison."

In a very short while — although it seemed an eternity to Edison — his letter was answered by Mina's father. He gave his consent both happily and quickly. The inventor sighed with relief, because Mina had come to mean so much to him and he loved her with all his heart. At times, he thought of poor Mary and knew, without a doubt in his mind, that she would have wanted him to remarry. Then there were the children to consider — it was going to be much better for them to have the affection and care of a woman like Mina. Yes, this marriage would be a blessing to them all.

It was now the fall of 1886. Edison decided that his future bride should have the most beautiful residence in the world as her home. He asked her which sort of life she would enjoy the best — one in the country or the city. Mina lowered her soft eyes and replied without hesitation.

"The country," she murmured, smiling at her fiance.

Edison was delighted and immediately set out on a quest for

such a home. He finally located what he felt would please her and, on a cold winter's day, took Mina to see it. Snow had fallen and the drive to the residence was windy and bitter. Mina laughed all the way and held the inventor's hand tightly.

"Where is the house?" she asked, as they quietly traveled along.

Edison gave her a loving glance and a broad smile covered his face.

"In West Orange, New Jersey," he said. "It's beautiful."

The young woman was delighted and squeezed his hand a little tighter. In no time, they arrived at the home Edison had selected and Mina's face reflected total and complete surprise. There, sprawling before them, was a veritable castle of wood, brick and mortar. It was called Glenmont and had been built by a millionaire from New York, the inventor explained; the building cost of the house had come to $200,000 and was a staggering amount for those days. Edison had found that he could purchase the property for a fourth of that amount. Mina's eyes were wide with delight, but she felt he should not spend too much.

Edison took her inside the house and showed her its many rooms. They were enormous and boasted smooth paneling and skillfully done trim in the American Romantic style. As they glided from room to room, Edison knew for certain that Mina wanted the house and told her he would close the transaction.

On the drive back from West Orange, they talked rapidly of Glenmont and the thirteen acres upon which it sat. Mina laughed and chatted about decorating the place, while Edison chuckled at her girl-like enthusiasm.

"Think of the upstairs den," she exclaimed. "It will be such a retreat for you."

The inventor smiled and snuggled closer to her. She was always considerate of him and his welfare and for this, he was eternally grateful. Not many women had the gumption to live the life of an inventor's wife, but Mina was not like other women. His love for her was overwhelming.

Edison on the lawn of Glenmont, his home at West Orange

Within the next few weeks, time sped by quickly. Some of his co-workers, including Batchelor, gave the inventor a dinner in honor of the forthcoming wedding. Meanwhile, Mina was busy preparing for the event, as her parents promptly sent out stacks of ornate invitations.

Then the great day arrived. It was February of 1886. The Millers had decorated their elaborate home in Akron for the wedding. Flowers were profuse and the downstairs looked like a veritable bower. There was an orchestra playing for the guests in the front parlor and an entire crew of waiters stood by for the reception. On that memorable day, a prominent minister of the Methodist Church performed the ceremony which took place beneath a beautiful arch of roses. Thomas Alva Edison and Mina Miller smiled into one another's faces as the minister asked them to repeat the precious vows. Their look was one of rapture as the minister at last spoke the final binding vows.

"I pronounce you man and wife," he declared, then stepped aside as the many guests crowded around the happy couple.

At last Thomas Edison and Mina Miller were man and wife. It was to be a wonderful marriage which would endure through the next forty-five years and which — during days to come — would cause Mina Edison to express herself.

"You have no idea," she later exclaimed, "what it means to be married to a great man."

Mina Edison knew what it meant — and loved every minute of it. In the fruitful years to come, she was to be his constant and enduring inspiration. Her love, filled with understanding and encouragement, would endure many trying times. She was to manage the household operation of the vast Glenmont with the dignified touch of a queen. Her hours were to be lonely at times, while her illustrious husband labored in the massive laboratory close by.

The future was to make her a staunch and capable woman who literally became the inventor's ears, as total deafness slowly overcame him. The beautiful woman was to become his devoted companion and, in time, was regarded as the First Lady of in-

Mina Edison visits her famous husband at his laboratory

vention and industry. National leaders respected her and the public considered her as a lady of greatness. Through every experience, she was to remain at Edison's side, including that last and most final one — that of death.

Indeed, Mina Edison was to live a full and rich life with Thomas Edison. Together, they would march into the twilight years, forever remembering their beautiful wedding and the true meaning of their vows. The sweet memory of a rose-covered bower and the look of love upon her husband's face would remain with Mina Miller Edison forever.

And to the newly wedded couple, forever was to be a wonderful experience, as they walked through it hand in hand.

Courtesy Department of the Interior, National Park Service

The upstairs sitting room at Edison's home, Glenmont

The Yielding Years

NOW IN HIS EIGHTIES, the great old inventor sat quietly in the den at Glenmont. He loved to come here after a day's work and relax among the memorabilia. There were several comfortable chairs in the room, as well as a tufted sofa, and long shelves which held many of his books. The sprawling windows looked down upon the green lawn of the mansion and gave the old man a fine view of his acres. Today, having just enjoyed a light meal, he stood looking at the great trees in the distance.

The elderly inventor was reminded of a time, many years ago, when he had looked at this countryside with a friend. As they stood side by side, Edison shouted at his companion.

"Do you see that valley?"

The companion nodded. "Yes, it's a beautiful valley."

Edison waved a hand toward the lovely rolling landscape. He looked straight at his friend and shouted again, this time louder and with conviction.

"Well, I'm going to make it more beautiful. I'm going to dot it with factories."

This, then, was the beginning of the famed Edison West Orange Laboratory. A short while after his marriage, the inventor had begun construction of numerous brick buildings which would become famous throughout America and the world. It was to be the largest and best equipped private laboratory in existence. During its erection, Edison scribbled his opinion of the new laboratory in a notebook. In his bold handwriting the inventor spoke with gusto.

"I will have," said the notation, "the best equipped & largest

Courtesy Department of the Interior, National Park Service

The main laboratory and gatehouse at Edison's West Orange plant

Edison's library at the West Orange laboratory

laboratory extant, and the facilities incomparably superior to any other for rapid & cheap development of an invention & working it up into commercial shape with models patterns & special machinery. In fact there is no similar institution in existence. We do our own casting forgings. Can build anything from a lady's watch to a locomotive . . . Inventions that formerly took months & cost large sums can now be done 2 or 3 days with very small expense, as I shall carry a stock of almost every conceivable material."

The main building of the laboratory contained over 60,000 square feet. In it were housed huge machine shops, an engine room, pumping and glass-blowing rooms, stock rooms, photographic and chemical departments, and electrical testing rooms. The main wing of the enormous structure housed the library and large offices. The library alone was fantastic, housing 10,000 books neatly catalogued on the long shelves. The ceiling was thirty feet high and the room could be viewed from two tiers of galleries which looked down on the library floor. Dominating the scene was, of course, the old roll-top desk belonging to the renowned inventor.

Here, in such a fantastic setting, Thomas Edison labored until the close of his career. Within the walls of the West Orange laboratory great inventions were born and given to humanity. His work was untiring and he — to the public's mind — was always on the verge of discovery. In later years, the wise and aged inventor expressed his personal feeling about this sort of work.

"Discovery," he would exclaim, "is not invention, and I dislike to see the two words confounded. A discovery is more or less in the nature of an accident. A man walks along the road intending to catch the train. On the way his foot kicks against something and he sees a gold bracelet embedded in the dust. He has discovered that — certainly not invented it. He did not set out to find a bracelet, yet the value is just as great."

If pushed too far for an expression of his philosophies, he might turn on the amazed inquirer and shout at him.

"There is no substitution for hard work! Restlessness is discontent — and discontent is the first necessity of progress. Show me a thoroughly satisfied man — and I will show you a failure."

One of the first projects Edison attempted at West Orange was the development of his beloved phonograph. In a short while he had applied for over eighty patents which covered improvements of the famous speaking machine. The Edison shops hummed with activity as thousands of ornate phonographs were manufactured for public consumption. Millions of cylinders, containing all manner of music, were sold every year to eager buyers. This led Edison to the development of the office dictating machine, based on the same principle as the phonograph.

Here again was a lucrative field, and the shops were swamped with orders for the new dictating miracle. Every unit manufactured by the Edison plant bore the inventor's name, emblazoned in gold on the equipment. Not for a minute did the great inventor allow the public to forget that his genius had created these wonders.

He was forever battling ignorance and felt that man alone was responsible for his own failures.

"I've been in the inventor business for many years," he would exclaim, "and my experience is that for every problem the Lord has made He has also made a solution. If you and I can't find the solution, then let's honestly admit that you and I are damned fools, but why blame it on the Lord and say He created something impossible?"

In 1889, the aging inventor struck upon a startling idea. Because he had invented a machine that could talk, he wondered if he could not make pictures that moved! Thus far in photographic history, there had been only still photographs. It was true that a few had tinkered with the idea of pictures that moved, but to little or no success. Edison proceeded to read up on the subject in the quiet of his library and felt that now, with this knowledge, he could actually create motion pictures.

His next step was to visit with the pioneer of the photographic industry, George Eastman of Rochester, New York. Edison placed an order with Eastman for an unusually long roll of celluloid film to be shipped to West Orange as soon as possible. The inventor,

Thomas Edison in his West Orange laboratory

according to earlier calculations, figured that if a series of photographs could be taken at the rate of fifteen per second, then they would reproduce — when shown on a special projector — in a lifelike manner.

First of all, he must invent a movie camera. This he did after months of experimenting almost in secret. He labored from early until late, trying all sorts of lenses and intricate mechanisms; finally, after untold hours of probing and sweat, he came up with a satisfactory camera. This machine was quite bulky for its day and represented a revolutionary step in the art of photography.

Edison paused in his labors to comment on the project. His voice fairly shouted with enthusiasm.

"I am experimenting upon an instrument which does for the eye what the phonograph does for the ear, which is the recording and reproduction of things in motion, and in such form as to be both cheap, practical and convenient. This apparatus I call a Kinetoscope."

Next on his schedule was the creation of a new motion picture projector. This task was approached with the same determined zeal as the camera and finally bore fruit in 1889. With the projector in hand, Edison started experiments with the new film George Eastman had manufactured and found, much to his delight, that his concept of movies was a success. The first flickering film was a simple one — that of an Edison employee, John Ott, in the act of sneezing.

Now that he had progressed this far, the inventor decided to build a studio in which to make his films. This crude structure, erected on the grounds of the West Orange laboratory, was constructed of wood and was covered with tar paper; the entire building was mounted on a revolving pivot foundation so that the sunlight might be captured through its lift-type roof. The studio was appropriately named "The Black Maria."

By this time, the year 1894 had rolled around. Edison became quite elated over his new invention and plunged into the making of films. One of the early productions was an exciting fight sequence between "Gentleman Jim" Corbett and an unknown

Edison demonstrates his motion picture projector

pugilist. Other unusual movies made inside the funereal "Black Maria" included "Buffalo Bill" and a cast of menacing Indians, a troop of French ballet girls, dangerous knife throwers, bouncing acrobats and the muscular strong man, Sandow. Even though the movements flickered dimly on the screen, the films were both new and enjoyable to that generation.

As time went by and Edison made further improvements in his motion picture camera and projector, he felt they might be better used for educational purposes. His opinions on this subject were quite candid and to the point.

"I firmly believe," he said, "that the moving picture is destined to bear an important part in the education of the future. One may devote pages to the descriptions of the processes of nature to be learned by rote in the schools. Suppose instead that we show to the child the stages of that process of nature — the cocoon itself, the picture of the cocoon unfolding, the butterfly actually emerging. The knowledge which comes from the actual seeing is worth-while. The geography which comes from travel is better than the geography of the books; the next thing to travel is following the same scenes through the moving picture."

It was not too long until the great inventor thought of teaming up two of his brilliant inventions — the phonograph and the moving picture. It occurred to him that the next step in this photographic revolution was to combine both sight and sound, thus creating an even more realistic image upon the screen. This was accomplished by Edison in a relatively short while and his excitement was high as he sat through the first sound movie. In later years, stooped and worn by the passage of time, he commented upon this miraculous feat.

"My plan," he shouted, "was to synchronize the camera and the phonograph so as to record sounds when the pictures were made, and reproduce the two in harmony. As a matter of fact, we did a lot of work along this line, and my talking pictures were shown in many theatres in the United States and foreign countries. I even worked on the possibility of an entire performance of grand opera, for example, being given in this way. Another

Courtesy McGraw-Edison Company

"The Black Maria," Edison's first motion picture studio, at West Orange

thought I had was that such a dual arrangement might record both the lives and the voices of the great men and women of the world. Can you realize the tremendous impetus this would be to the study of history and economics?"

With the invention of the motion picture camera and projector completed, Edison now turned to other fields of endeavor. In 1891, he had begun a task which would lead him to his first — and final — failure. The project was that of iron-ore extraction. On drafting paper, he developed a new method of obtaining concentrated iron ore by magnetic separation; huge ore-bearing stones — according to his theory — would be dropped between two tremendous roll-type crushers, thus grinding the boulders into dust. When magnetism was applied to this fine dust, the iron would be immediately drawn out and separated from the remaining and useless ore. There was no doubt in his mind that the scheme would work.

Edison immediately called for a magnetic survey in the East to locate the largest sources of ore-bearing rock. The results of that survey were stupendous. In later years, Edison looked back on the reports he had received, his old head shaking with a degree of regret.

"The results," he mused, "amazed me. They were simply fabulous. There was untold wealth lying all around us. In three thousand acres immediately surrounding us, in New Jersey, there were over 200,000,000 tons of low-grade ore. I leased 16,000 acres near by, which contained sufficient ore to supply the whole United States, and leave a surplus for export, for more than seventy years."

Edison, before tackling the problem of ore supply, had grown alarmed at the probable scarcity of the element in this country. Most of the mining was then carried on out West and his hope was to find a means of extracting the ore in other parts of the country. In the event of war, iron ore would be in great demand and a virtual necessity for survival.

He immediately started work on the project in New Jersey, calling the tract of land "Edison." Soon, Edison, New Jersey,

Edison sitting at the office of his ore
plant in Edison, New Jersey

hummed to the sound of construction and the familiar figure of the inventor was forever checking all parts of the plant. In not too long a time, the mine was — according to the inventor's scheme — producing the iron ore in satisfactory quantities. But before long, delays and accidents on the job began to hinder operations. Edison, long-faced and scowling, became dissatisfied with the results. He began to pour more money into the improvement of his mining plant and spent more and more of his precious time on his sixteen thousand acres.

After the passage of nine years of desperate labor, Edison was shocked to find that a new deposit of iron had been discovered in the Mesaba mountains of Minnesota. The deposit was so tremendous, that it could supply the United States for untold years with high-grade ore at a cheap cost. Edison shook with disappointment. The great inventor was defeated — almost bankrupt.

His venture in the mining field had cost him over $2,000,000 of his own money. Even now, debts were piled high on a fruitless venture which, in the near future, stood deserted and empty like a ghost town. But he was undaunted, and spoke of recouping to a company employee.

"We have got to make enough money," he muttered, "to pay off our debt. No company in which I have been personally responsible has ever failed to pay its debts. I do not propose to allow this to be an exception."

With true vigor, he forgot the magnetic ore separation scheme and turned to other activities. The great inventor became interested in the manufacture of Portland cement, and, using lessons he had learned in the former enterprise, soon opened a plant of his own. Everyone felt it would be doomed to failure; but surprisingly enough, the cement plant was a great success and soon helped Edison back on his feet, financially. Out of the gigantic kilns, came the cement which built Yankee Stadium in New York City; huge office buildings, immense industrial plants, bridges and even homes — all came from the new and improved Edison cement. The genius of the inventor had risen again to conquer his recent failure.

Thomas Edison, the Wizard of West Orange

Back at the West Orange laboratory, he experimented night and day. His hours were backbreaking, but Edison's spirit was determined. His remarkable mind traversed from one subject to another, probing and digging into all facets of life and industry. For a time, he became interested in the workings of the X-ray, as originally discovered by Roentgen in 1895. From this source, and through his own genius, he created a new device called the fluoroscope. Edison did not patent this invention, but gave it over to public domain to be used in medical and surgical research; but from his intense study of the powerful fluoroscope, he developed a new concept of artificial lighting which he called the fluorescent lamp. On May 16th, he applied for a patent covering this new form of light, then laid it aside to plunge into other busy activities.

Unexpectedly, in the busy year of 1896, sadness again touched the heart of Thomas Edison. While working with the fluoroscope, he received word that his father had died. With the old man's passing, the inventor felt that all remnants of his youth had also passed away. He recalled with tender feeling those long-ago days in Port Huron and the many times Samuel Edison was to punish him for childish misdeeds. Now, those days were gone forever, leaving only a faint memory of that frozen frontier and the love of his devoted parents. Samuel and Nancy were united again in the vastness of eternity and their beloved son would claim them only in memory. With a heavy heart, Edison returned to his work and the opportunity to achieve a further success which would have pleased his parents.

He also realized that his own life was perhaps on the waning side. He was near fifty now and there was no way to know how many years were left. His energy never failed and, with the exception of minor ailments, Edison's health was almost perfect. Time was always an elusive element to him, so he plunged even farther into work, cramming every spare minute with experimentation or research.

The next several years found Edison engaged in a variety of activities and his inventions were countless. In 1900 he began what was to be a ten-year search for a successful storage battery; when finally completed, it was to be the driving force in transportation — operating railway car lighting and air conditioning, inter-plant transportation, mine haulage and hundreds of other industrial uses. The countless months of work on the storage battery resulted in fame for the inventor and cash in the laboratory till.

Afterward, his applications on new inventions marched to the patent office like rows of paper soldiers: an improvement on long rotary kilns for cement production . . . a universal electric motor for operating dictating machines . . . the production and improvement of the disc phonograph record, replacing the old traditional cylinder . . . electric safety lanterns for miners working in the dark interior of the earth . . . a new process for the manufacture of carbolic acid and a design of a tremendous plant to manufacture this acid for the United States. Indeed, they were busy and eventful years, bringing the inventor little rest, but an unforgettable satisfaction. His contributions to human progress were astounding and his fellow men continuously expressed their satisfaction with his work.

His laboratory and plant at West Orange surged with activity. The manufacturing segment of his work was overwhelming and the employees were forever busy. Not only did the plant produce phonographs, dictating machines and improvements in motion pictures, but many other items such as the new improved storage battery. Edison was absolute monarch of his enterprise and was informed of every activity in the business. He marched from building to building, inspecting the products which bore his famous name. Manufacturing was kept at the most economical level possible and the slightest deviation from the inventor's instruction brought down his wrath. West Orange was a focal point of creativity and industry — Thomas Edison was determined that it remain that way.

Meanwhile, outside the confines of the laboratory, the world situation was dark. Germany was soon to declare war on the United States. It was now 1914 and President Woodrow Wilson called for the aid of every American in the possibility of a struggle. Edison found himself thinking of the destruction war could bring and, to a man who created for good, it was a horrible thought. For years he had labored to bring lifesaving devices into the world — now a threat of death-dealing machines faced him and his countrymen. He knew that war would diminish the demand for his manufactured goods and that America faced a tremendous economic situation.

About five months after the beginning of the war across the sea, tragedy struck the inventor with devastating force. On the night of December 9, 1914, a fire unexpectedly broke out in his West Orange plant. The flames and smoke rose into the sky like reflections from Hades. The flames licked at the brick buildings and devoured six of them before dawn; seven other concrete structures were completely gutted by the fire, leaving the interiors dark and smoldering with heat. Edison, at home when the fire began, rushed to the scene and began to dig through the rubble of ruins. Among the items clutched from the fire was a portrait of the inventor. He looked at it for a moment, then laughed. With a pencil, he wrote deliberately across the face of it: "Never touched me!"

The next morning, standing in an immense pile of scorched rubbish, Edison surveyed the scene. He turned to an assistant and shouted through the devastation.

"Well, she's a goner, but we'll build her bigger and better than before!"

Before another thirty-six hours had passed, Edison issued instructions for the building of a new plant and marched off with confidence. In no time, the ruins of destruction were replaced by new brick units designed to withstand the ravages of fire. The enterprise of Thomas Edison was soon back in operation and the employees were at work again.

When he had time to think about it, Edison returned to the menace of the war. Being an old electrician — he was past sixty by now — he felt that this field would play an important part in any conflict. Marching up and down his library at West Orange, he expounded on the subject with authority.

Edison replies to a letter of sympathy regarding
the fire at his plant in 1914

"Electricity," he firmly stated, "will play an important part in the wars of the future. Torpedo boats can be dispatched two miles ahead of a man-at-war and kept at that distance under absolute control, ready to blow up anything within reach. I believe, too, that aerial torpedo boats will fly over the enemy's ships and drop a hundred pounds of dynamite down on them. A five-million-dollar war vessel can be destroyed instantly by one of these torpedoes. I can also conceive of dynamite guns."

He would pause in his pacing, running a hand through the bushy gray hair. His eyes were almost sad as he continued his comments about war.

"I have no intention of ever devising machines for annihilation, but I know what can be done with them. Nitroglycerin is one of the most dangerous substances that man can deal with. Touch a drop of it with a hammer and you will blow yourself into the hereafter. Iodide of nitrogen is even more dangerous. While experimenting with explosives in magnetic mining, I made some of them so sensitive that they would go off if shouted at. Place a drop on the table and yell at it and it will explode."

In Washington, Josephus Daniels — then Secretary of the Navy — felt that the great inventor could be of invaluable aid in the event of war. He immediately wrote Edison an intense letter, asking him to head up a Board of Advisors on national defense. Before replying, the inventor made a trip to The World's Fair in San Francisco. With him and Mrs. Edison were Henry Ford and his wife and the leader of the rubber industry, Harvey Firestone. The party enjoyed the expansive fair and exhibits, pausing to visit with the famed horticulturist, Luther Burbank, at Santa Rosa. Once the brief trip was completed, Edison returned to West Orange and the matter of the government's proposal. Not being in favor of anything bent to destruction, Edison gave the subject hours of thought. Finally, with his sense of patriotic duty overwhelming him, he told Secretary Daniels that he would accept.

After the sinking of the S. S. "Lusitania" on May 7, 1915, it was clear that the United States could not stay out of the war. Secretary Daniels rushed to Glenmont and went into a private

Edison inspects a naval submarine, during World War I

huddle with Edison, mapping out a plan of operation. Upon Daniels' return to Washington, the inventor commenced his study of American defense units and weapons. Thomas Edison began his association with the government by immediately investigating the defense weapons in existence.

During the bitter conflict, he traveled by land and by sea. His inspections took him aboard ships and submarines. He was forever asking questions of the military and studying their answers with care. For two years, his full time was taken with inventions and improvements for the nation's defense. The list was tremendous and impressive: plans for saving cargo boats from submarines . . . hydrogen detectors for submarines . . . telephone systems aboard ships . . . airplane detection . . . underwater searchlights . . . coast patrol with submarine buoys . . . the detection of submarines by sound from moving ships . . . a sound-ranging method of locating the position of guns . . . turbine heads for projectiles . . . a preventive of rust on submarines and guns . . . and induction balance for submarine detection.

The roster of inventions amounted to forty or more. In later years, the inventor recalled his work for the government with a smile. His old eyes gleamed as he spoke of the dubious results.

"I made about forty-five inventions during the war, all perfectly good ones, and they pigeon-holed every one of them. The Naval officer resents any interference by civilians. Those fellows are a closed corporation . . . I do not believe there is more than one creative mind produced at Annapolis in three years. If Naval officers are to control it the result will be zero."

When at last the war came to an end, Edison continued on at West Orange with a sense of permanence. Now he could resume his normal work. It was 1918 and time to take up the task of building. During the war, he had learned a great deal about the value of creating instead of demolishing. As he stood beside a stained and worn worktable at the laboratory, he paused to express himself on this subject.

"It is curious," he muttered, "that the better impulses of our humanity do not work hard to spread their careful, helpful

Edison in his West Orange laboratory,
holding an Edison-Effect lamp

thought as the less worthy elements do to spread their evil thought and foolish reasoning. If this could be reversed, the world very quickly would become a better place to live in."

And Thomas Edison, using his reasoning and genius for good, would devote the last years of his life to making the world a better place to live in.

It was his creed . . . a personal Declaration of Independence from drudgery and suffering.

To a man who does not carry a watch, time can be a fleeting thing. Before he is aware of it, the hours — indeed, the years — can fly past until one day he faces the twilight of his life. This experience came to the industrious Edison as he labored at West Orange on his humanitarian inventions. His life, thus far, had been filled with hard work and ingenious goals; the countless discoveries and inventions had contributed much to the benefit of his fellow man. There had been setbacks and disappointments, to be sure, but he had mastered these with his usual determination. Much of his life had been spent in the field of electrical development, probing the secrets of nature with zeal and enthusiasm. Now, as old age crept up on him, he felt that other areas of endeavor might lead him to discoveries of a different sort — discoveries that might also prove to be blessings for the world.

During the early twenties, Edison continued his work at West Orange in much of a routine manner. He finally decided to give up the manufacture of the phonograph and records. The majority of former production was called to an abrupt halt, and the industry which bore his name became limited in its activity. Now, past seventy years of age, his mind still was alert and conscious of new ideas and enterprises.

"I have had sixty years of mechanics and physics," he said one day, in a moment of reflection. The time had come to look into other areas of research and experimentation.

His family became gradually alarmed at his state of health. He now had three children by his wonderful wife: Charles, Madeleine and Theodore, each a blessing to the aging inventor. These,

Mina Miller Edison in her later years

Thomas Edison in his seventies

together with the children of his first marriage — Marion, Thomas, Jr., and William L. — were constantly concerned about his long hours and the tremendous load he carried. Most of the boys had worked at the laboratory with the inventor and carried their share of the responsibility.

Charles Edison gradually assumed the helm of the industry, allowing his father more time for personal work and research. But as the years had sped past, the entire family felt that Edison should slow down, and set a more reasonable pace for himself. With his usual flair for independence, he promptly ignored their pleas.

"Everything," he would shout, "comes to him who hustles while he waits."

More and more often, Edison and his wife journeyed to the winter home in Florida. The warmth of the sunshine seeped into the inventor's bones, as he tried to relax in Fort Myers. But even here, he continued his work with deep interest and activity. On occasion, he would invite the Henry Fords and Harvey Firestone to join him in the sunny retreat. Great times were had by the intimate group, as they sat by the river and reminisced about the good old days.

After one of these visits, Henry Ford expressed an interest in synthetic rubber. In the past, Edison, Ford and Firestone had traveled to California together to see the famed horticulturist, Luther Burbank. On one such trip, Edison had remarked that our rubber supply would be cut off if the United States became involved in war again. Ford immediately asked the inventor if he might be able to come up with a synthetic substitute. The aging Edison looked at him with interest.

"I will some day," he replied and resumed his conversation with Burbank.

Down in Florida, the subject had come up again and set Edison to thinking. This might be the field of endeavor he had been searching for. It was far different from mechanics or electricity and would result in benefaction for his country. Lately, his health had begun to wane. He was now eighty years old. The once staunch body had become invaded by diabetes and the onslaught of a gastric ulcer. He ate lightly and drank a great amount of milk, always ignoring the threat of illness. If he devoted time to a search for synthetic rubber, perhaps there would not be too much physical strain. He could work most of the time from a chair beside his workbench. At least, for the moment, it seemed the soundest reasoning.

So it was that, in the winter of 1927, he journeyed to Fort Myers to take up the search for synthetic rubber. Mina Edison went with him, managing their Florida home with her customary efficiency. Her every thought was for the aging inventor's well-being and she strove constantly to protect him. When Ford or Firestone traveled down to see how their friend's work had progressed, Mrs. Edison always was the smiling and perfect hostess. She adored her famous husband and her only goal was his happiness.

Edison began his search by collecting all manner of plant life. He knew from past reading that many plants contained a source of rubber. His problem was to find one which, at an economical cost, would yield the most rubber per acre. The Fort Myers laboratory became swamped with samples of all sorts and sizes; the inventor's assistants labored long hours, cataloging every stem and leaf. Their aged chief sat in his wooden chair, bent over with keen observant eyes, as they yelled questions at him. His deafness was now almost total and the only way to communicate with him was to shout.

The work continued for months. Edison was extremely happy in this new field of work. It was of a different nature and kept his enthusiasm at a high level. He joyously examined the species of plants like a happy schoolboy, muttering to himself as he worked. By the close of the second year, he had checked over 14,000 plants and had found that about six hundred of them contained rubber. From the frame laboratory in Florida, the aged inventor reported some progress to those interested in his work.

"Everything looks favorable to a solution," he said, returning once more to the stacks of stalks and samples.

Edison's winter laboratory at Fort Myers, Florida

(As restored at Henry Ford's Greenfield Village, Dearborn, Michigan)

Photograph by the author

Edison shows Harvey Firestone results of his rubber experiments at the Fort Myers laboratory

In not too long a time — and through constant checking — he discovered that goldenrod contained about five per cent rubber. Encouraged by this finding, he began to crossbreed varieties of goldenrod and developed a tremendous new breed which grew to fourteen feet. From this, Edison was able to extract a yield of twelve per cent latex. At last it seemed that success was forthcoming and the old inventor was delighted.

"We are just beginning," he wheezed and began to calculate the rubber extract from acres of goldenrod. He dreamed of obtaining nearly a hundred and fifty pounds of rubber from each solid acre of the giant plants. There was absolutely no doubt in his aging mind that he could accomplish this feat.

In the summer of 1929, the great inventor returned for a short visit to his West Orange laboratory. While there, his digestive tract became upset and he was confined to bed with diabetes and a kidney disorder. In a matter of days, Edison got to his feet again, hoping to return to Fort Myers and the perfection of his synthetic rubber.

"Give me five years," he said, "and the United States will have a rubber crop."

But he was not to have five more years.

His health was definitely on the decline. The stomach disorder became more acute and the old man's memory became slightly foggy. His anger was easily evoked over seemingly little things and he shouted at the top of his voice. Employees were more subject to his wrath if they disobeyed him or performed an experiment incorrectly. He was forever muttering about "bonehead moves" and refused his family's plea to slow down. In all truth, the aged inventor was beginning to act like a shaggy old lion, roaring at the least provocation.

Finally, after months of crossbreeding and grafting, the shuffling inventor was able to produce a small quantity of his new and costly rubber. He had it crated and shipped to Harvey Firestone who, upon receipt of the bulky synthetic, had it molded into tires for Edison's Model-A Ford touring car.

The old inventor was pleased with the results of his work.

His notebooks were crammed with shakily written notations of the experiments. He paused to comment cheerfully about the rubber project.

"We have reached the point," he said, "where we can say that our experiments have proved successful . . . the possibilities are almost unlimited when the principle is once established."

Edison's statement regarding his discovery of synthetic rubber met with little enthusiasm. The press treated it lightly, as though it was one of his lesser discoveries. The old man was running down like an unwound clock. His capacity for endurance was slim and his energies failed him more frequently. Because of his past brilliance, he was treated with respect and admiration; but everyone knew that his endurance was fading and that the old mind was getting dim.

He left Fort Myers and returned to his home in West Orange. More and more of his time was spent away from the laboratory. Mina Edison cared for him with tenderness and urged him to rest, while she continued to quietly operate Glenmont. She sat at her desk, punching buttons on the telephone and issuing soft-spoken orders. Hanging on the wall in her room were two precious photographs: one was of her famous husband at the age of twenty and the other was of Charles, their eldest son. She often gazed at the portraits before returning to her busy duties.

The old inventor sat in the den upstairs for longer periods of time. He seemed quite oblivious of his surroundings these days. Mina Edison worried about him and tried to keep his interests alive and working. She had about given up, realizing that his synthetic rubber discovery would probably be his last. Her husband was a sick man.

Then Henry Ford came to visit his old friend. Mina Edison regained hope, for with the coming of Ford, there was also the chance to interest her husband in the future. The fiftieth anniversary of the invention of the electric light was to take place in October of 1929. Henry Ford, secretly and happily, was planning a great jubilee for the occasion and had come to ask for Edison's participation.

The old man, weak and bent, peered into Ford's eyes. He reached out a feeble hand and slowly got to his feet.

"And what do you propose to do?" asked the aged inventor.

Ford paused before answering. A broad and intense smile spread across his face.

"Restore your old Menlo Park laboratory in every original detail," he said, "so that on this glorious occasion, you can bring light back into the world once again."

The old inventor shook his white head.

"Menlo Park," he whispered, and fell gently back into his chair.

Decline Of A Dynamo

THE OLD INVENTOR lay huddled in his warm bed at Glenmont. The great white head lay sunken in a soft pillow and the eyes — now dim with age — stared at the ceiling. There was not a sound in the room, except for his own labored breathing. Outside the window, the radiance of fall had turned the hills to orange and amber-like hues. The sky was clear blue and, except for the winging of a bird, there was no movement. The venerated inventor was alone with his misty thoughts as the past once again merged with the present.

The name Menlo Park echoed in his faint memory. Slowly, he recalled the brilliance of Light's Golden Jubilee and the unforgettable re-creation of his electric lamp. Through the fog of memory, images were taking shape, as though he were reliving that magnificent night of honor. He dimly remembered the conversation with Henry Ford and the great things he was planning for the Jubilee. The industrialist had always admired Edison and felt that this anniversary of the electric light should be a special occasion. After their visit at West Orange, Ford promptly returned to Dearborn, Michigan — where his mighty plants were located — and began an intense plan for the forthcoming festival in October.

Secretly, he purchased all of the old land Edison had owned at Menlo Park. When the titles were transferred, Ford appeared in the New Jersey hamlet to look around. After all these years, nothing remained of the once famous laboratory or any of the other buildings. When Edison moved to New York in 1885, the original clapboard structure fell into disuse; at one time, it was used as a church, then a dance hall and finally, in its last stages

Edison's Menlo Park laboratory, as restored at Henry Ford's Greenfield Village

of deterioration, as a chicken shed. Neighboring farmers began to strip the lumber from the building to use in patch-up jobs on their homes and barns. The old brick machine shop had been demolished, as had the library and office building. Only the foundations of these once famed buildings were left.

Henry Ford realized that he needed technical assistance in the restoration of Edison's Menlo Park. In this year of 1929, there was only one living survivor of the original Menlo Park staff — it was Francis Jehl, who for forty years had been in Europe. Edison had sent him there to establish lighting systems in foreign countries and Jehl had devoted these many years to the task. Henry Ford spared no expense in locating the one-time laboratory assistant and was able to engage him for the restoration job.

Francis Jehl then worked side by side with Ford as the days sped past. They made frequent trips to the old tract in New Jersey, scouring every inch of land for remnants and relics. On one such trip, Ford discovered the old mortar and pestle which Edison used on the chest of drawers in the laboratory; it was broken and buried in the ground when the industrialist found it. He removed every piece available and took it home where he, himself, glued it back together. Every shred of old lamps that could be found vas shipped back to Dearborn.

There, on a tremendous acreage selected by Ford, workmen labored almost around the clock building a new yet antique village. The industrialist had decided to create a real community consisting of restored buildings collected from various parts of America; streets were being laid out, as well as sidewalks and a village green, which, in turn was flanked by a chapel and a town hall. Here, for visitors to marvel at, were such restored buildings as the Wright Brothers' Cycle Shop . . . a jewelry store . . . tintype studio . . . general store . . . printing shop . . . sawmills . . . carriage shop . . . toll house . . . blacksmith shop . . . McGuffey schoolhouse . . . cotton gin mill and a fire house. It was a gigantic project which, upon completion, cost about ten million dollars. Ford named the community Greenfield Village.

Next to this re-creation of early American life, he constructed

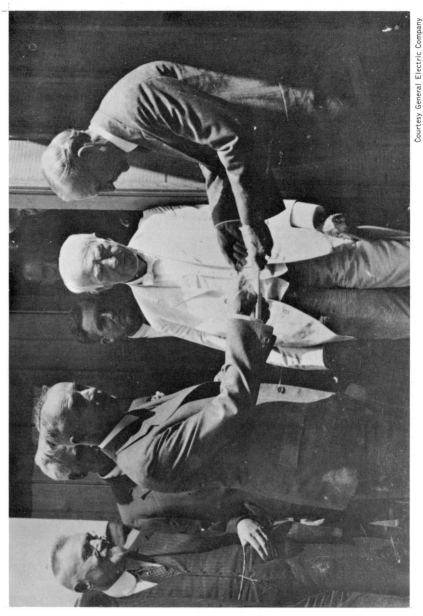

Presentation of the original Menlo Park "Glass House" to Henry Ford for restoration at Greenfield Village.

a huge museum, which was housed in a replica of Independence Hall. It was here that he planned a gorgeous banquet for Edison on the night of Light's Golden Jubilee. The other surprises for the aged inventor would be the buildings in the village which were associated with his past. Ford had carefully moved — with Edison's permission — one of the frame laboratories from Fort Myers; he had the original Smith's Creek station moved to Greenfield, just as it appeared in the Grand Trunk Railway days. Then — as a crowning achievement — there was the reconstructed Menlo Park group.

By now, Ford had scoured the New Jersey countryside, purchasing every scrap of lumber that was once a part of the old laboratory. With Jehl's help, he reconstructed the laboratory in every detail, as well as the brick machine shop, the library and even Sarah Jordan's boardinghouse. Years ago the glass house had been claimed by General Electric and rested on their grounds in Schenectady; when it was discovered that Ford planned a Jubilee for the old inventor, General Electric presented the glass house to him for removal to Greenfield Village. Every dirt street in the lavish project was lined with lamp posts containing replicas of Edison's first lamp. Even carloads of the original soil at Menlo Park were shipped to the village and spread around the reconstructed laboratory. In a word, Henry Ford's re-creation was complete and perfect in every minute detail.

Two days before the big event, Edison arrived in Dearborn. His appearance was that of a seriously ill man, but he was delighted at the miracles Ford had performed. He was taken through the village on a special tour, while Ford explained — with waving arms — the origins of every shop, home and tavern. The old man was delighted with the wondrous village, exclaiming like a schoolboy over the sights he beheld.

Then, with vast pride and pleasure, Ford opened the gate to the Menlo Park compound. Edison was dumbfounded. In every complete detail, his once busy and famous laboratory stood before his very eyes. There were the machine shop and the little glass house and his library — everything exactly as it had been

Edison, Henry Ford and Francis Jehl in the restored Menlo
Park laboratory at Greenfield Village

(Edison prepares a carbon filament for a replica of his first lamp, to be used at Light's Golden Jubilee)

in 1879! What a marvel to behold for the aged and feeble inventor. Tears came to his eyes as he walked up the dirt path leading to the laboratory. Then, of a sudden, he came to a halt.

Coming down the steps, with arms outstretched, was Francis Jehl. Dear Francis! The two old men had not seen one another in over 40 years and their excitement was high. When Jehl reached his famous employer, the two embraced one another in tenderness and esteem. Edison, with tears streaming down his cheek, expressed his deep delight at seeing his assistant once more — the only survivor of that beloved group who labored here.

Jehl and Ford ushered the inventor into the restored laboratory and thence to the second floor. It was all here — the chest of drawers, the organ, the pot-bellied stove, the Sprengel pump, and every worktable in accurate detail. The shelves lining the room contained exact replicas of every chemical bottle Edison had ever used; he saw, resting in their old places, the first phonograph and copies of the original platinum lamp, as well as his great invention of the electric light. Edison's emotion was almost uncontrollable. He turned from the wondrous sight and, with laughter in his voice, shouted at Ford.

"Well, you've got this just about ninety-nine and one half per cent perfect."

Ford, who had been so meticulous about the reconstruction, was alarmed. He turned to Edison, his brow wrinkled in puzzlement.

"What is the matter with the other one half per cent?" he asked.

The old inventor laughed again and looked about him.

"Well," he said, "we never kept it as clean as this!"

After this special showing for Edison, the Jubilee took place two nights later. The replica of Independence Hall was lighted by candlelight as the world-famous guests arrived for the festival. They came from around the world to pay tribute to the great Edison and his contributions to humanity. President Herbert Hoover journeyed from Washington and was in attendance, happy to participate in this festival honoring his friend.

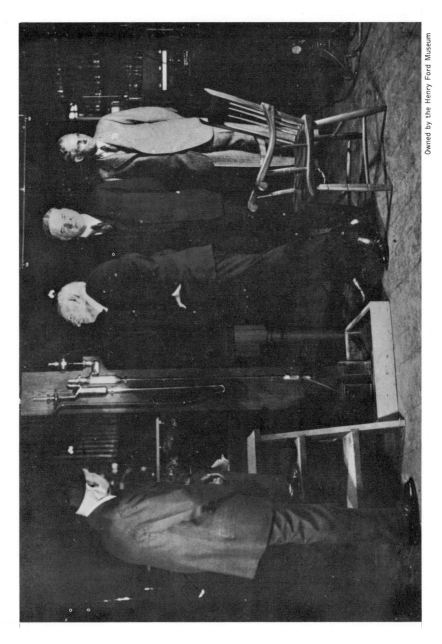

Francis Jehl, Thomas Edison, Herbert Hoover and Henry Ford at Light's Golden Jubilee

Before the banquet, Edison — along with Ford, Jehl and Herbert Hoover — drove to the darkened Menlo Park laboratory. It was raining that night as they wheeled to the restored buildings in a carriage. On the second floor of the famed laboratory, everything was in readiness; overhead, the gas jets cast dim shadows about the room, just as they had done back in 1879. The President stood beside Edison, Ford and Jehl at the restored Sprengel pump. On its extension arm was a replica of the first electric light, waiting to be ignited by its inventor. Also on the second floor was a radio commentator who broadcast every movement of the famous group to the nation.

Edison and Jehl approached the pump and muttered together. The former assistant — now a man in his seventies — mounted the wood stepladder and poured mercury into the glass tubing. Slowly, it trickled down, creating a vacuum in the glass bulb. When ready, Jehl signaled his old chief. Edison, with shuffling movements, walked to the switch beside the pump and paused for a moment.

The excited radio commentator talked rapidly into his microphone.

"The lamp is now ready," he reported, "as it was a half century ago! Will it light? Will it burn? Edison touches the wire."

As he spoke, the inventor reached with a bony hand for the switch. Glancing at Jehl, he hesitated a moment, then slowly threw the switch. Of a sudden, the replica of his original lamp flared with brilliance, lighting the laboratory like that long-ago night in 1879. The announcer fairly shouted into his microphone.

"Ladies and gentlemen — it lights! Light's Golden Jubilee has come to a triumphant climax!"

At that very same moment, the lights in the village were glowing like fireflies in the night. The replica of Independence Hall was illuminated with a sudden burst of magnificence, causing the famous guests to exclaim with delight. Truly, it was an unforgettable sight and a just honor to Thomas Edison, the grand old man of invention.

After the re-enactment, Edison returned to the banquet hall

in the company of his notable companions. He hesitated at the door before joining the celebration, his face white and pasty. His emotions had no doubt gotten the best of him for the moment. Mrs. Edison led her husband to a settee, urging him to rest for a while. The old man looked at her as though in pain, and then he began to cry.

"I won't go in," he whispered.

A glass of warm milk was brought to him immediately. He drank it slowly, then feebly got to his feet. A thrilling ovation was given him as Edison shuffled to the head table, surrounded by admirers and friends. All during the evening, he sat with his white head sunk with fatigue — he ate nothing and was unable to hear any of the tributes.

President Hoover rose to his feet and, glancing at the inventor, delivered a brief message of praise.

"I have," he said, "thought it fitting for the President of the United States to take part in paying honor to one of our greatest Americans . . . Mr. Edison has repelled the darkness . . . has brought to our country great distinction throughout the world . . ."

As Hoover spoke, the aged inventor cupped a hand to his ear, but it was useless. He could hear nothing. He sat quietly until his own time had come to speak. With great effort, he rose from the chair and stood shakily upon his feet.

"This experience makes me realize as never before," he wheezed, "that Americans are sentimental and this crowning event of Light's Golden Jubilee fills me with gratitude. As to Henry Ford, words are inadequate to express my feelings. I can only say to you, that in the fullest and richest meaning of the term — he is my friend. Good night."

With that, he slumped down in his chair and his face was drained of color. President Hoover's physician rushed to the old man's side and led him from the speaker's table. Immediately, he was taken to Ford's home and put to bed with hopes of his recuperation. Edison peered up from the pillows and whispered quietly.

"I am tired of all the glory, I want to get back to work."

Light's Golden Jubilee was finished . . . and with it, the career of Thomas Alva Edison.

Death was beckoning to him from the mists.

Back home at Glenmont, the old man's health failed him rapidly. Uremic poisoning had spread through the once staunch body, leaving him weak and forgetful. Now he was confined to his bed and visitors were kept at a minimum. Mina Edison hovered near her husband, holding his withered hand and doing everything possible for his comfort. It was now October of 1931. To the feeble inventor, snuggled beneath the blankets, it seemed impossible that the Jubilee had taken place two years ago. There was no way to account for the time. Even though he never carried a watch, the second hand of life had ticked away until now, confined and aged, he faced the mystery of death. When the doctors came to check his condition, he insisted on measuring out his own doses of medicine and was forever checking the medical chart. To the very end, he was an experimenter and a lover of nature's secrets.

Finally, his condition worsened. There was no doubt now — Thomas Edison was dying. The family slipped into the quiet room to look at him, then departed with tears in their eyes. Reporters gathered at Glenmont, anxious for reports of the old man's weakening condition. They were informed periodically by Charles Edison that his father was worse and the end was near.

Mina, still beautiful in her twilight years, seldom left her husband's side. Sitting near him, she often leaned over to inquire if there was anything she could do.

"Are you suffering?" she asked him, tearfully.

The grand old man slowly turned on his pillow. His eyes — now faded and tired — looked at her lovingly.

"No," he whispered, "just waiting . . . just waiting."

On October 17th, the inventor's pulse dropped and he went into a deep coma. Prior to this, he had gazed out of the window for a moment, peering at the rolling hills. In a muted and choked voice, he had spoken for the last time.

THOMAS ALVA EDISON, DYNAMO OF INGENUITY

"It is very beautiful over there."

Now, the entire family was called to the death room. The great inventor was scarcely breathing and the faint sighs tugged at his children's hearts. It was Sunday, the eighteenth, and the hour was near three in the morning. At the stroke of 3:24 A.M., the beloved Edison's quiet breathing ceased. The room was in solemn silence as the physician stepped forward to examine the still body of the inventor. He listened intently for a moment, then stood erect, his face drawn with fatigue.

"The end has come," he whispered, and moved away from the bed, quietly.

Thomas Alva Edison, age eighty-four, was dead. He had now embarked upon his last great discovery — the secret of eternal life. In his fabulous past, he had been a veritable living dynamo of production. His inventions, brilliant and humanitarian in scope, were to be remembered with affection forever. On this morning of October 18, 1931, their creator — the laughing, probing, searching man with the sparkling eyes — lay white and still.

The dynamo was dead . . . but his light still burned.

INDEX

(Page numbers in *italic* refer to illustrations)